SOCIAL INSECT
POPULATIONS

SOCIAL INSECT POPULATIONS

By

M. V. BRIAN

The Nature Conservancy
Furzebrook Research Station
Dorset, England

1965

ACADEMIC PRESS · LONDON · NEW YORK

ACADEMIC PRESS INC. (LONDON) LTD
BERKELEY SQUARE HOUSE
BERKELEY SQUARE
LONDON, W.I

U.S. Edition published by
ACADEMIC PRESS INC.
I I I FIFTH AVENUE
NEW YORK, NEW YORK 10003

Library of Congress Catalog Card Number: 65–28621

Printed in Great Britain
by W. & J. Mackay & Co Ltd, Chatham, Kent

PREFACE

This book is an attempt to bring together a large number of dis-connected observations on populations of social insects and to encourage a comparative approach in the future. Population is simply one of several possible measures of the status of a species; it is naturally influenced in many ways and it would be easy to extend the scope of this book to cover a much larger part of the biology of social insects. This has, however, been avoided as far as possible, for such important subjects as foraging and feeding behaviour or caste determination have recently been thoroughly reviewed by others.

I should like to thank Dr. J. B. Cragg for his encouragement and to acknowledge the invaluable help of Miss M. Hale, Miss J. V. Hibble and Miss A. Kelly.

October 1965

M. V. BRIAN

CONTENTS

CHAPTER 1

INTRODUCTION

It is over 20 years since this subject was comprehensively reviewed by Bodenheimer (1937a) and Emerson (1939). Ants, bees, and wasps predominate in the discussion, but termites are mentioned and the European honey-bee *Apis mellifera* L., although not wild, is also brought in, as it has been the subject of a great deal of ecological work recently.

Social insects are interesting ecologically, since they combine certain characteristics of plants and animals. They are sedentary, but their range is less restricted than that of plants, and unlike many animals they do not have to carry their whole body wherever they go. Like some animals they have achieved homoiothermy, and those that have not have the means of living in the hottest microzones available. Their units are comparable in size and metabolic rate with medium-sized mammals and large birds. In fact, they form an important and characteristic factor in most ecosystems.

A. EVOLUTION

The evolution of social life has been discussed by Brereton (1962), Hamilton (1963, 1964a and b), Kalmus (1964), Michener (1964), and Maynard Smith (1964). Natural selection is able to effect socialization of relatives, as mutual protection and co-operation enhance the survival not of individuals but of the gene replicas they carry. This has been called "kin selection" by Maynard Smith, who has pointed out that though no reproductive barriers are needed they do help. Hamilton has suggested that the haplodiploid method of sex-determination characteristic of Hymenoptera is particularly favourable to social evolution, and may account for its repeated origin in the group. Thus, whereas mothers and daughters share $\frac{1}{2}$ their genes, sisters have $\frac{3}{4}$ in common, and a daughter is better employed helping her mother to produce another offspring than doing so herself.

This theory also provides a plausible explanation of why males are not socialized in Hymenoptera, though they are in Isoptera. The degree of relationship between males and their daughters is $\frac{1}{2}$ and to their brothers and sisters $\frac{1}{4}$, so that to help to produce these would not improve their "inclusive fitness", but in termites male and female are the same in their degree of relationship with offspring as with sibs, namely $\frac{1}{2}$. Also explained is the fact that workers frequently continue to lay male-producing eggs in Hymenoptera, for the relation of female to son is $\frac{1}{2}$ and of female to brother only $\frac{1}{4}$. Apparently the fact that males are only haploid biases the selection process against them, for they contribute only half as much as females to the gene pool in each generation.

Whilst the theory explains the matrifilial evolution of social life, it runs into difficulties with multiple insemination and pleometrosis (defined by Richards and Richards, 1951), both of which reduce the degree of relationship in a society. As regards the former, if the female is mated by more than two males there is nothing to gain from altruistic behaviour. Though in this case any tendency to multiple insemination after the evolution of a worker caste might not be very disturbing. To overcome these difficulties, Hamilton has suggested a high viscosity in the populations and a stable climate, which would, by increasing inbreeding, enhance the degree of relationship. There is also the possibility of group selection (Maynard Smith, 1964). This depends on the spread of a characteristic to all members of the group by genetic drift; some degree of reproductive isolation is also essential. Maynard Smith gives a possible model which shows that if the individuals of a group avoid reproducing at high densities so as to conserve their food supply they can persist, even with some periodic mixing, with populations which are improvident and wholly aggressive. As there is likely to be, in pleometrotic colonies of social insects, a high degree of relationship, possibly even sistership, and as the populations are closed for long periods and as new queens are often perhaps always daughters of the original queen(s), then conditions seem to be satisfied. Moreover, if the colony fragments with growth it is conceivable that the progeny of different original mothers will move off into separate buds. Presumably, regression of caste differences will be prevented by the greater efficiency of differentiated populations and their greater spread, provided they can maintain an equilibrium with their resources.

Wilson (1963a) has shown that the effective population size (defined Li, 1955) of colonies of social insects is:

$$4n_t \; \bar{m} \; \bar{q}/n_c(1 + \bar{m})$$

when n_t = number of individuals
  n_c = colony size
  $\bar{m}$ = average number of males fertilizing one female
  $\bar{q}$ = average number of queens.

This tends to $4n_t\bar{q}/n_c$ when $\bar{m}$ is large. Increase in $\bar{q}$ will normally be restrained by the optimal worker/queen ratio.

B. ORGANIZATION AND CONTROL

The social insects are variously organized, some into distinct colonies which are closed to others of the same and different species, some into colonies that are diffuse and only closed to members of other species or subspecies; and there are all forms of intermediates (Scherba, 1964). The initial production of non-reproductive, working individuals, common to all societies, is essentially the establishment of a positive feed-back system that may be expected to lead in due course to a greater growth of population per individual (specific growth rate) than could have occurred without any social organization. The progeny of the queen(s) are so guarded, in what amounts to an extension of parental to sibling care, that not only may they be expected to produce far more offspring than they would as non-social insects (alone), but more than all their daughters together could in the same area. This is because, in theory, the social organization enables the effective collection and pooling of resources and the adjustment of the rate of reproduction to this, by some mechanism that involves less waste than could arise in a non-social population.

The latest views on the subject of population control are summarized by Varley (1963), Klomp (1964), and Solomon (1964). Density, independent factors like weather, traffic, fire, and other hazards (Browning, 1963), cause major fluctuations and may be termed key factors (Morris, 1959), but they are not regulatory. They have not been considered in this review. These fluctuations are damped in the ecosystem by many interactions with other species (competitors, predators, and parasites) which act at different stages of the life cycle and of which only a few appear to be necessary for control. In addition, there is intraspecific competition and self-spacing behaviour, the latter aimed at reducing competition (Brereton, 1962; Wynne-Edwards, 1962; Klomp, 1964) and distributing the population in relation to its resources.

In this review after enumerating some actual densities the development of populations is considered first in an ideal environment, then in progressively more realistic ones. In the last section a tentative consideration of the population control of a few selected species is attempted.

CHAPTER 2

NUMBERS AND DENSITY

Social insect populations are best expressed as individuals per unit area, though if colonies are clear cut the number per colony is also useful. An important ratio is that of non-reproductives/reproductives. To enumerate brood stages as though they were equivalent to adults is misleading, but often difficult to avoid in termites.

A. METHODS OF ESTIMATION

Direct counts of colonies in winter, or at night in summer, may be obtained, but there are many unknown sources of error and the colony is normally destroyed. Sometimes estimates can be made from the traffic associated. Army ants can be estimated during migration in this way (Raignier and van Boven, 1955; Rettenmeyer, 1963a). Holt (1955) has assayed the foraging population of *Formica rufa* L. from traffic flow and the circuiting of marked workers; theoretically the number of foragers is the product of the number of trips completed in a given time (the flow past a point) and the harmonic mean duration of all trips (obtained from the marked ants); the first averaged 370 a minute and the second 160 minutes giving 59×10^3 foragers. Within a single species this may be a useful index of activity.

Recently, mark-recapture methods have been applied, but again there are many sources of error. External marks are removed by ants and termites, though suitable for bees and wasps. This is especially serious if a radioisotope is used, for the grooming ants acquire the marks they remove; it must be firmly held in the internal tissues. This can be achieved by feeding the isotope in syrup and waiting several days for assimilation to be complete when the risk of transmission to others is negligible. It must then be ascertained by suitable experiment whether the longevity or activity of the marked workers is altered and whether in returning to their colony they disperse randomly. A further difficulty is obtaining a random sample from a population of several age groups that may behave differently. This can sometimes be partially overcome by attracting the whole colony into artificial nest sites, and extracting samples over a considerable area of nest, and sometimes by baiting with food, provided it has been shown that all age groups come to baits. The results should, of course, be checked against direct counts if these can be obtained with any accuracy.

B. THE NUMBERS IN COLONIES

1. Bees

Groups of the primitive bee *Allodapula* average 2 females and there is evidence that they co-operate (Michener, 1962). Halictine bee societies range from 4 up to some hundreds (Michener, 1958; Plateau-Quenu, 1962). *Bombus* overlap this range (Cumber, 1949a) and are smaller in the arctic, where the active season is shorter, than in the tropics (Richards, 1927a). Michener and Laberge (1954) have recorded one of 2 183 workers in the neotropics. There is a general correlation within the genus between social complexity and colony size (Sladen, 1912) which Medler (1957) has recently illustrated in relation to North American species. He collated data for 8 surface-nesting relatively primitive species and 4 deep-nesting more advanced ones and got 37–191 in the first and 150–450 in the second case. Meliponine bees range from less than 100 up to many thousands (Michener, 1958), *Apis florea* Fabricius has colonies of $4-5 \times 10^3$ (Butler, 1954a), and *A. mellifera* L. in captivity may reach 7×10^4 in favourable circumstances (Bodenheimer, 1937b).

2. Wasps

Many wasps' nests have been counted. In their study of South American Polybiinae, Richards and Richards (1951) counted 11 nests of 2 species of *Polistes*, a primitive genus and found a maximum around 20; 33 nests of short-cycle Polybiinae averaged 132 and reached 721. An exceptional nest of *Protopolybia pumila* (Spin.) had 7×10^3 workers and intermediates. Data on the European *Vespula* group have recently been summarized by Kemper and Döhring (1961): 8 nests of the hornet *Vespa crabro* L. averaged 100 and reached 400; 6 nests of the relatively primitive *Dolichovespula sylvestris* Scopoli averaged 95 and reached 180; 23 nests of the advanced *Paravespula vulgaris* L. averaged 10^3 and reached 2 847, and 18 nests of *P. germanica* F. averaged 1 613 and reached 3 377. Again there is a general correlation between social complexity and colony size.

3. Ants

Ant colonies vary between a few hundreds and millions. The primitive subfamily Myrmeciinae rarely exceed 200, though *Myrmecia gulosa* Fabricius with 1 586 has been recorded (Haskins and Haskins, 1950). The same is true for most Ponerinae except the legionary *Leptogenys purpurea* Emery, which reaches 2×10^3 (Wilson, 1959a), and it is a general rule that legionary species have bigger colonies than closely related non-legionary ones (Wilson, 1958a). Many colonies of Myrmicinae have been accurately counted: the genus *Leptothorax* has colonies of less than 100 (Headley, 1943; Talbot, 1957a), so, too, many dacetine ants (Wilson, 1953b, 1962e). *Aphaenogaster* has several hundreds (Headley, 1949; Talbot, 1951, 1954), *Myrmica* likewise (Talbot, 1945; Brian, 1950), but the more advanced genera reach several thousands (Wheeler, 1937; Roonwal, 1954; Golley and Gentry, 1964; Wildermuth and Davis in Weber, 1959). Formicinae range in the genus *Formica* from the simple *F. fusca* L. with several hundreds up to *F. rufa* with 3×10^5 (Pickles, 1938; Talbot, 1948; Ayre, 1957; Pavan, 1959, 1962). *Lasius flavus* Fabricius has given numbers of the order of 10^4 (Waloff and Blackith, 1962; Odum and Pontin, 1961) and *Oecophylla* in the order of 10^5 (Ledoux, 1950; Way, 1954a; Vanderplank, 1960). But the Dorylinae can claim the record at present, with $2 \cdot 0 - 2 \cdot 2 \times 10^7$ for *Dorylus* (*Anomma*) *wilverthi*, Emery (Raignier and van Boven, 1955). The genus *Eciton* only reach 10^6 (Schneirla, 1957; Rettenmeyer, 1963a). Evidently their well-organized nomadism compensates for their primitive feeding method (hunting). In his study of ant-colony size in tropical rain forest in New Guinea Wilson (1959a) found that even in the higher subfamilies colonies were rarely larger than 100 individuals, though it was a general rule that the more primitive ponerine, cerapachine, and myrmicine species had smaller colonies than the dolichoderine, formicine, and doryline ones. Also tree dwellers had larger colonies than the ground dwellers, but this again was confounded with social and evolutionary complexity as the more advanced subfamilies were more arboreal.

4. *Termites*

Termites range from a few thousands in the primitive Calotermitidae (Kalshoven, 1930; Grassé, 1949; Lüscher, 1961) to numbers in the order of 10^6 (Grassé, 1949; Holdaway, Gay and Greaves, 1935; Gay and Greaves, 1940).

C. DENSITY AND BIOMASS

1. *Bees*

The economic density (Elton, 1932) of bees is difficult to measure. *Bombus*, for example, has been shown to "home" if moved 450 m (*B. agrorum* Fabricius) or 1 200 m (*B. lapidarius* L.) according to Free and Butler (1959), so that areas foraged will be of the order of 10 or 100 ha respectively. To assess the nest population on areas of this size is extremely difficult. It is customary, in fact, to record the foraging density, though this is very variable (Bingefors *et al.*, 1960; Fridén, 1960, 1961; Eskilsson and Fridén, 1962). The economic density of *Apis mellifera* does not present the same problem, but it has less meaning ecologically in view of their domestication, which involves food supplements and seasonal hive movements. However, Nilsson (1959) mentioned 8–10 colonies/ha on *Trifolium pratense* L. (red clover) and 6 on *T. repens* L. (white clover) in Sweden, and Levin and Glowska-Konopacka (1963) mention 5 colonies/ha on *Medicago sativa* L. (lucerne) in North America. Assuming average populations per hive, this gives some 30 females/m² or 3g/m². This is a substantial figure, but compares reasonably well with Weaver's (1957) observation of 4 foraging bees/m² on *Vicia villosa* Roth.

2. Ants

(a) *Woodland*. In general, the number of colonies of ants in a given area is inversely proportional to their size, which tends to reduce the variability of individual density. Headley (1943) counted the colonies of ants nesting in acorns on the floor of a mixed wood in Ohio which had very few herbs. On 46·5 m², 58 nests were found (41 *Leptothorax longispinosus* Roger, 13 *L. curvispinosus* Mayr, and 4 nests of 3 other species), giving a density of 1·25 nests or 67 females/m². In a dense *Robinia pseudoacacia* L. wood in Ohio which allowed flickering sunlight on to a rich herb stratum consisting mainly of *Lactuca spicata* Headley (1952) found 11·1 colonies/m² with 10 species of ant, a much richer fauna, but the female density was not computed. About two-thirds of the nests were *Ponera coarcta* Latreille (7·2/m²). The soil stratum of a mixed oak-hickory wood (*Quercus rubra* L., *Q. alba* L., and *Carya ovata* (Mill.) K. Koch) in Missouri, rich in herbs and shrubs, yielded 16 species of ant (30% *Aphaenogaster rudis* Emery, 20% *Ponera coarcta*, and 20% *Amblypone pallipes* Haldeman), giving an average of 6·1 colonies/m², again a rich fauna, but the density of females is not recorded (Talbot, 1957b). These are all remarkably high colony densities. No doubt the colonies were small, perhaps less than 100 individuals each, and the workers foraged both above and below their nests.

The presence of the wood ant *Formica rufa* and its allies in European woodland probably reduces the diversity of species considerably. *F. polyctena* Foerst. in Germany has 4 nests/ha (Gösswald, 1957), 7/ha (Bruns, 1960a), 6–8/ha in Harz oak woods (Otto, 1958b), 1–2/ha in virgin forest in the Alps, and 6–7/ha in plantations near by (Adeli, 1962). Hunting areas of 220–3 360 m² are recorded of *F. rufa* (Eckstein, 1937), and this at a rate of 3 × 10⁵ workers per colony gives densities as high as 710 females or about 7·1 g/m². Writing of species of the *Formica rufa* group in Siberian forest, Marikovsky (1962b) records a high-density "colonial form" with about 180 nests/ha and estimates

4237 ants/m², a remarkable and probably exceptional economic density. These insects range throughout the strata of the woodland. In tropical clove and coconut plantations near Zanzibar, Way (1954b) has calculated 625 females/m² for *Oecophylla longinoda* Latreille. Each colony covers some 800 m² and again they forage throughout the strata. Finally colonies of the army ant *Dorylus (Anomma) wilverthi* living in the Congo equatorial forest may cover 4–5 ha (Raignier and van Boven, 1955) and two can live close together. As each colony may have 22 × 10⁶ workers, this gives about 500 females/m². This species keeps to a fairly definite stratum near the soil surface. It is worth noting that these last three woodland ants (with the exception of Marikovsky's estimate), even though one is temperate and the other tropical, have economic densities of the same order. Moreover, the doryline ant, though having larger colonies, does not have a greater economic density.

(*b*) *Grassland*. In an old field in Michigan, Talbot (1953) found 17 species of which the 3 principals occurred at the rates (in colonies/m²): 0·50, *Lasius niger neoniger* Emery; 0·23, *Myrmica americana* Weber; 0·18, *Solenopsis molesta* Say. The first had a maximum of 3·3 colonies/m² in one plot. The species most studied, *Aphaenogaster treatae* Ford, had 0·06 colonies/m² and an average of 38 workers/m², not a high density. In Wyoming, an island in the Snake River with *Artemisia cana* meadow, had a population of 400 *Formica opaciventris* Emery nests for 3 years giving 0·007 nests/m² and a maximum of 0·04/m², but unfortunately the density of individuals is not available (Scherba, 1963). In an old field in British Columbia the species *Formica subnitens* Creighton, whose foraging areas averaged 233 m², gave about 90 females/m² (Ayre, 1957). In Scottish acid grassland four species of ant (*Formica lemani* Bondroit, *Myrmica ruginodis* Nyl., *M. scabrinodis* Nyl., and *Leptothorax acervorum* Fabricius) reached densities of 5–11 nests/m², but had economic densities of 0·7/m² (Brian, 1956b). This means about 700 females or some 3·0 g/m², a value comparable with the dominant ants of woodland just mentioned. In English neutral grassland the main species is *Lasius flavus* and Waloff and Blackith (1962) found a maximum density of 0·6 mounds/m². Applying the figures already given, one can obtain 6–15 × 10³ females/m², a very high density, which implies some 15 g/m². Odum and Pontin (1961) give 1130/m² in a similar habitat which amounts to 1·4 g/m². Over larger areas including *Lasius niger* L. they found 485 or 0·06 g/m². All these figures are larger than Pickles's (1937) estimate of 0·008 g/m² for this species, but there is no doubt that the populations will vary enormously with the nature and productivity of the grassland ecosystem. However, it is probably true to say that *L. flavus* may reach densities greater even than the monospecific populations of woodland ants.

Some data are available for dry grassland and desert ants. *Veromessor pergandei* (Mayr) has 15 colonies/ha in a Californian desert (Tevis, 1958). Numbers of workers were not estimated, but were thought to be fewer than where vegetation perennated. *Pogonomyrmex barbatus* F. Smith in Texas has 21 mounds/ha (Box, 1960), and *P. badius* Latreille in South Carolina has 27 hills/ha (Golley and Gentry, 1964). At 4500 workers per hill this gives 12 females/m^2 representing some 0·084 g/m^2 of the ant, a low figure.

All these comparisons have been based on nearly monospecific populations. Many more standardized data are necessary if the densities of polyspecific populations in different ecosystems are to be compared.

CHAPTER 3

REPRODUCTION

Colonies reproduce in two principal ways. They may emit sexuals that mate and start new ones or they may grow and break up into parts. In the first case the income of an established colony is largely converted into sexuals, whereas in the latter it is converted into workers, only such sexuals being made as are necessary to maintain a suitable ratio with the non-reproductive castes. In the first case the chances of finding new sites is maximized by providing as many sexuals as possible, each equipped with the best possible guidance mechanisms. In the second case the parent colony itself explores the environment and plants a bud if suitable space can be found. In cases when workers are apterous this second method necessarily reduces the distance that can be moved at each generation. Some forms reproduce in both these ways.

At this stage we are not concerned with the consequences of over-crowding such colonies.

A. BY SINGLE QUEENS (OR PAIRS)

1. Queen foraging

The programme followed by a queen (or pair) founding a nest is vital to her success. Hypothetical evolutionary stages from solitary to social wasps have been traced by Richards and Richards (1951). Here they will be illustrated by recent work on bees. In most pre-social Hymenoptera the female parent constructs a cell, provisions it, lays in it, seals it, and moves off to start a new cycle somewhere else; or sometimes a new cycle may be started contiguous to the first one, which thereby gains a measure of protection from enemies. This is the system employed by most Halictine bees: thus *Halictus calceatus* Scopoli produces up to 8 bees in this way in the first group (Plateau-Quénu, 1964) and *Lasioglossum zephyrum* (Smith) makes 5 cells and then rests for 6 to 8 weeks whilst they mature (Batra, 1964).

A slightly more complicated procedure is when new cells are started near the first before it is completed. It appears that *Halictus duplex* Dalla Torre, a social species, is of this type (Sakagami and Hayashida, 1960), for each parent makes some 4 cells which are lined, provisioned, laid in and closed, but the brood though it varies in its degree of development does not do so as much as it would if the cells were made sequentially. This system, logically evolved, leads to the formation of a set of cells which are provisioned, laid in, and sealed, and which has the advantage of providing the parent with a set of worker assistants all at once and of enabling her activities to be temporally specialized. This system is followed by *Halictus marginatus* Brullé, which makes a set of some 3 cells, provisions them all, lays in them all, and seals them (Plateau-Quénu, 1962). This "cell set" system, as it will be called, introduces a new behaviour feature: that of fixing the size of the clutch (3 or 4 in *H. marginatus*) so that as many workers as possible are made in the minimum time.

One way of reducing the time before help arrives is to lay the eggs as soon as the cells are made or, even better, when only their foundations are laid (wasps), or to lay all the eggs in a roughly made cell and add partitions later on (some *Bombus*). When the eggs hatch food can be brought in as needed. In more primitive systems, even though the cell was stocked with food at first, this may have been examined periodically for quality, as Batra (1964) has recently found in *Lasioglossum zephyrum*. In any case, infertile eggs need replacing.

Although this gives an early start, it is still important not to make too many cells to begin with, for by the time the larvae are at their largest and most voracious the parent may be unable to feed them adequately. This is the critical stage, for shortly afterwards they metamorphose and need no help. Once the optimal clutch has been laid a parent is best occupied defending and regulating the temperature of the nest or collecting and storing materials that will later be needed. Progressive provisioning is particularly helpful in situations where food is short. It is not necessarily an attribute of social insects, for as it cuts down the generation time it enhances the reproductive potential of solitary forms directly, and indeed it is shown by a few species that make cells sequentially (Wheeler, 1922). It is, however, characteristic of social types that have evolved the cell set system of starting colonies probably because, when there are many cells, time is not wasted waiting for larvae to digest and assimilate their food. Apparent exceptions to this rule are the meliponid bees, which provision each cell fully at the start. These bees, however, reproduce by fission and even provision their new site beforehand so that food and labour is not desperately short, and to feed in one lot is more efficient than in instalments each of which necessitates prior inspection and leads to the possibility of seriously replicated and redundant effort.

In the European *Polistes gallicus* L., only the foundations of cells are made before eggs are laid. Some 19 cells and 18 eggs may be produced in about 10 days before the first egg hatches (Deleurance, 1957). When this happens the larvae are fed on eggs that the queen continues to lay and other younger peripheral eggs are consumed as well. The cells are progressively extended as the larvae grow. Only 9 hatching over a period of 5 days reached the pupal stage, after which more cells were made. This species is sometimes pleometrotic.

Morimoto (1954a, b, c; 1959) confirmed these observations with the haplometrotic *P. chinensis antennalis* Pérez, and also noted that empty cells were not filled during the feeding stage, though he concluded that the queen did not lay during this period. Only queens in warm situations resumed cell making and laying after the first lot had pupated. Some 5–10 progeny resulted, but there were 30–40 cells before the first worker emerged. The critical nature of this early stage is well shown by Yoshikawa's (1954) study of the same *Polistes* species. All but 2 of 69 nests of *P. fadwigae* Dalla Torre were left by the queen before workers hatched, and to judge from the brood destruction, they were starving.

Like the above, *Dolichovespula sylvestris* is haplometrotic, but it builds envelopes round the brood cells which raise the temperature a few degrees (Brian and Brian, 1952). The procedure does not differ much from that of *Polistes*. Many cells are built at first, but only a few after the eggs have hatched; again more cells are added once some larvae have pupated and by day 22 when the first workers emerge there are some 30–45 cells—far more than would be thought necessary for the production of only 5–15 (8·3 average) pupae. As with *Polistes*, there is evidence that peripheral eggs are eaten and many peripheral larvae are undoubtedly starved, not simply because the queen is overtaxed, but because once a few pupae have matured she stops collecting food, though it is not certain that this is a direct response to pupae as such. These larvae survive and produce small workers under the care of much larger queen-fed workers and though not wasted they are a sign of inefficiency, for it could be argued that the time and energy devoted to their culture would be better spent making envelopes. Envelope making is started when only a few cells have been made, and is the first activity to be discontinued sometimes when the first larvae hatch, sometimes after pupae have formed. As many as 4 may be made, and the most successful nest under observation had 4 on day 13. The growth of colonies of *Vespa orientalis* L. is very similar (Darchen, 1964), though this species appears to feed small larvae as well as eggs to larger ones.

Bombus lays a set of about 12 eggs in a single cell (Sladen, 1912). The cell is primed with pollen, but when the eggs hatch after about 4 days more food is given (both solid and liquid) at intervals. Larvae of some species become separated into individual cells and each pupa makes its own cocoon. Adults emerge after 22 days, in time to help feed the second batch of larvae. The nest is heat insulated with a wax envelope and fibrous vegetation and the queen keeps the temperature a few degrees above ambient (Cumber, 1949a), lying with her body pressed into a groove between the cocoons. This bee appears to have evolved an efficient programme aimed at the rapid and effective rearing of relatively few workers.

Primitive ants (Myrmeciinae) start colonies by making a chamber, laying a set of eggs on the floor and bringing in food when it is needed; there is no priming with food as in Bombus. *Myrmecia forficata* Fabricius lays about 8 eggs which may take 120 days to give 3 workers (Haskins and Haskins, 1950). *M. regularis* Crawley lays about 10 eggs which give about 3 workers in some 150–250 days. The slowness is characteristic of both primitive ants and termites, and contrasts with bees and wasps, but what part incubation and the temperature of the site chosen plays is uncertain. Unlike the queens of higher ants, these do not eat their eggs.

Primitive termites (Calotermitidae) excavate nests in wood which serves also as food, and as it is not nutritious the colonies grow very slowly at first: *Cryptotermes havilandi* Sjöstedt lays 4 eggs and *Calotermes flavicollis* Fabr. 6 or 7 (Lüscher 1951). The latter lays eggs over a period of 30–35 days and then rests for 10–40 days and lays again (Grassé and Noirot, 1958a). Some 50–60 days elapse before the first egg hatches and then about 12 young appear and are fed at first on secretions, though later they eat wood. After a further period of egg laying there may be 55 individuals of various ages at the end of one year. Though there is periodicity it is not clearly related to the social situation. Unlike ants, soldiers appear early, in fact some 65 % of the first progeny are soldiers; but their frequency declines to about 3 % as the colony grows (Lüscher, 1961). Also in this family, *Neotermes tectonae* Damm., a tropical wood-eater, starts its colonies with sexual pairs in the deadwood of tree crowns; these grow very slowly and have only 30–60 workers and 3–7 soldiers in 1–2 years (Kalshoven, 1959).

Reticulitermes hesperus Banks (Rhinotermitidae), also a wood-eater, has been studied in detail by Weesner (1956). Like *C. flavicollis*, it starts very slowly and for 30–40 days no eggs are laid at all; after 150 days there are only 9–13 and incubation takes 50–56 days. First and second instars pass quickly (17 and 20 days respectively), but the third is very variable (18 days to 6 months). Its duration increases with population density, a fact which Weesner thought might be due to competition for adult secretions or enhanced activity in large groups (though by this stage the larvae are eating a good deal of wood). Soldiers were more common in smaller groups. Again there is some periodicity.

Cubitermes ugandensis Fuller (Termitidae) eats soil and the young are fed mainly by the male on stomodaeal food (as in *Reticulitermes lucifugus*

Rossi according to Buchli, 1950). Williams (1959a) found that a period of comparatively rapid egg laying (1 every $1\frac{1}{2}$ days) started about the 5th day and went on for about 3 weeks and then stopped. Workers appeared after 122 days, the maximum number being 12. Unfortunately the soil deteriorated and was not replaced.

2. *Queen with store*

In advanced ants and termites not only the fat body but also the wing musculature is converted into either eggs or exocrine secretions, both of which serve as food; there is also the special case of the fungus ants (Attini) that carry spores and so establish fungus gardens on which their first larvae feed (Wheeler, 1922). In ants the transition to "claustral" foundation takes place in the Ponerinae and has two associated features: the first set of workers are abnormally small, as presumably more small ones are better value than a few large ones, and the eggs adhere in a cluster and can be carried and protected as a single object (Haskins and Haskins, 1950, 1951). But the hatching larvae eat neighbouring eggs, for in the first instar they have sickle-shaped mandibles that easily puncture eggs and they can move a little (cf. insect parasitoids, Salt, 1961). To compensate for this far more eggs are laid than survive, so that eggs become a sort of food store.

Queens of the fairly primitive Myrmicine ant, *Myrmica rubra* L., lay about 25 eggs, but these only generate some 5 larvae and 3 workers either in the same year, after at least 9 weeks, or in the next year (Brian, 1951). They are thus, in spite of the egg food store, as slow as primitive ants. The egg number falls to zero as larvae hatch and it only rises again when pupation starts, but it is uncertain whether the queen lays throughout this period. *M. rubra* is known to practise secondary pleometrosis and the successful initiation of colonies by single queens may only rarely be accomplished in nature. *Crematogaster scutellaris* Oliv. is similar; single queens can produce workers in a season April to September (Soulié, 1962), though they more often join groups of workers budded from a colony. They appear to accept any queen of the right species provided she is fertile. *Tetramorium caespitum* L. (Myrmicinae) investigated by Poldi (1963) has a similar programme which, beginning after an early flight in June–July, produces workers in 30 days (exceptionally) or 45 (more usually), that is, in the same summer. After about 5 days eggs are laid and by day 15 there may be between 45 and 100 from a single queen, depending on her size. As in *Myrmica*, these drop in number suddenly as larvae hatch, since many are eaten directly. The queen also eats a few, but she more often eats larvae and pupae towards the end of the claustral period. An average of 12 pupae occur at the pupal maximum, indicating that about 10 workers could come from the first batch. These are much smaller relative to the queen than *Myrmica* workers.

Of the advanced formicine ant, *Oecophylla longinoda*, which lives at 25°C or more day and night in the tropics, Ledoux (1950) says that some 25 eggs are laid in a mass, that they hatch in about 5 or 6 days, and that no more eggs are then laid. Only one in four reaches the adult stage (comparable with *Myrmica*) in some 39 days. Way (1954a) confirms this, but Vanderplank (1960) had an average of 65 eggs per queen and in natural conditions 4 a day during the first week. He records the developmental periods of brood stages at various temperatures: at 33·3°C all larvae died and at 16°C though eggs were laid none hatched. At 30°C only 18 days were needed from egg to adult: in near natural climatic conditions some 21–23 days were needed, at least a week less than *Tetramorium caespitum* in Italy.

Lasius niger of the same subfamily has been weighed and counted during foundation by Yoshioka (1952), who supplied only water. The queen lost 15·6 mg in 35 days, yet due to water intake the brood weighed 25·7 mg. The exponential equation $n = ct^3$ was fitted to brood weight (n) and time (t) and the parabolic equation

$$m = m_0 + at + bt^2$$

to the queen's weight (m) and time (t) relationship (b negative). Combining these gave for the total weight of the system ($n + m$), a third-degree polynominal. Assuming that water uptake was through the egg shell and that eggs were limited in number, Yoshioka developed a model of weight/time relations that accorded reasonably with reality. However, it seems likely that the queen drank water and passed it to the eggs during oogenesis, as Poldi (1963) found in *Tetramorium caespitum*.

Like ants, higher termites form a chamber in soil and feed the first brood on body reserves. Lüscher (1951) found that of various tropical species tested those of the family Termitidae produced more eggs. *Tenuirostritermes tenuirostris* (Desneux) in laboratory conditions, starting only 3 days after pairing, laid about 5 eggs a day at first, but fewer later, so that by day 30 about 60 were present; young hatched on day 35 (Light and Weesner, 1955). Growth was rapid owing to the nutritive value of the saliva and some 60 days from pairing the first workers foraged for dead grass. Nasute soldiers formed 25–33% of the first brood. Colonies of a fungus-growing macro-termitine species *Ancistrotermes guineaensis* (Silvestri) were started in the laboratory by Sands (1960). As with *T. tenuirostris*, egg laying was initially rapid: 5 a day for 10 days with a sharp decline to 1 or less afterwards. These took 30 days to hatch and yielded small workers and soldiers (pigmented) on day 60; larger workers came a few days later. They did not break out until day 75 and started fungus combs of faecal pellets on day 80, though these were sterile until some mycelium of the correct strain (from a nest of the same species of termite) was added to the culture.

Termites thus parallel ants, with the possible difference that fewer eggs and more exocrine secretions are used as food. The claustral method, with reserves carried to the site from the parent nest in the bodies of adult sexuals, speeds the growth and reduces the time to feedback by workers and so improves the chances of successful colony establishment.

B. BY GROUPS OF QUEENS

In dense populations queens are likely to meet whilst site hunting. They may associate on equal terms, establish a hierarchy, or fight and disperse. If queens are unable to find their own nest sites, it is better that they help those that have already found them, particularly if they are genetically related to the foundress, as there appears to be some evidence that they often are (Hamilton, 1964a and b), for this favours the evolution of altruistic behaviour and hence of caste differentiation and more complex organization.

As already pointed out, all vespine and many *Polistes* wasps do not associate, and the same is true of bees of the genus *Bombus*, though Sladen (1912) found that sometimes two could be forced together. They then laid earlier (a group effect, perhaps), but after a while fought and even the victor neglected the brood.

Polistes nests in warm climates may collect a number of queens and especially in the early stages they may wander from nest to nest if these are numerous and close (Hamilton, 1964a and b). A hierarchy is established in each nest that has been exhaustively studied by Pardi, Deleurance, Gervet, Morimoto, and others (reviewed Brian, 1964a). It is not disputed that the top queen is more reproductive and the others more assimilative in function, but the way in which this develops is uncertain. Gervet (1962) has shown that a top queen lays more eggs if she has a companion, but a subordinate lays less. Some individuals will not lay at all without a companion. Thus grouping causes both stimulation and suppression, depending on the individual's relationships in the group structure. The top queen destroys the eggs laid by other queens which remain recognizable for some time (Gervet, 1964a and b, has begun an experimental analysis of this process).

Ant queens frequently associate to make chambers and lay eggs, but they often fight at the end of the brood-rearing period and establish haplometrotic colonies. No records of hierarchies appear to exist except a tentative suggestion by Poldi (1963) for *Tetramorium caespitum*, a species whose queens rarely associate. Poldi found that only sister queens would settle without fighting and once settled remained so even after workers had been produced. Waloff (1957) in studying *Lasius flavus* and *L. niger* found that queens co-operated in forming an egg-mass in a common chamber, though oviposition was a time of social tension as in *Polistes*. She found that fewer eggs were laid per queen and fewer eaten in groups, though the total number was greater. This might be due to a negative feed-back from the growing egg-mass that tends to stop oviposition once the right number of eggs have been laid. Or perhaps that sharing an egg-mass somehow reduces a positive stimulation to activity (including both feeding and laying) which it may exert, the queens in effect competing for space near the eggs. Further analysis of this situation should be interesting.

The reduced turnover could arise from the increased care given to the relatively fewer eggs, which defends them against disease, predators, and perhaps most important of all, hatching sisters. Queens survived better in groups, perhaps because they retained more reserves, perhaps because their mutual grooming was beneficial. Workers appeared in 4 months with 2 or 3 queens as compared with 7 months for single queens. Waloff suggested two reasons for this: either the first eggs were more likely to survive in a big egg-mass, fewer of whose eggs were eaten, or the better larval food supply improved growth rate (some matured in 13 as compared with 126 days).

So, by co-operating over construction, by pooling reserves, and by co-operating over hygiene and defence, the groups produced workers more quickly and certainly than single queens. They broke up when pupae appeared. The *Lasius niger* queens fought each other until only one survived with all the brood, but the *L. flavus* queens dispersed, each taking some brood. This was by no means equally shared and it is likely that some queens went without and died, so that in the end relatively few haplometrotic colonies were started. These might well have met later and fused with violence to all but one queen. Hamilton (1964a and b) has pointed out how this co-operation could evolve if *n* queens together had more than *n* times the chance of success that one has alone. Once they reach independence, however, altruism and some sociality can only evolve by kin selection if they are closely related (sisters, for example). For some reason *Lasius* but not *Tetramorium* queens co-operate advantageously.

Stumper (1962) suspects a stimulatory effect of grouping in *Camponotus vagus* Scopoli, for 2 queens together laid 25 eggs, which was more than twice as many as one alone. These gave 5 workers after 4 months, a typical performance. Queens of *Myrmica rubra* that failed to accumulate eggs alone did so immediately when grouped (Brian and Hibble, 1964), but in groups of different sizes the eggs per queen fell with group size as in *Lasius*. Evidently, as Gervet found in *Polistes*, there are stimulatory and depressive aspects to grouping which can act simultaneously and even differentially in relation to individuals.

Group foundation in termites does not seem to be recorded; perhaps bisexuality is an obstacle.

C. BY FISSION

Fission occurs in both pleo- and haplometrotic societies, though in the latter case it is associated with small-scale pleometrosis and presumably evolved by a progressive gain in degree of control over queen number. Tropical polybiine wasps have several queens and commonly reproduce in this way, either living for about 3 developmental periods and then breaking up (short cycle) or going on more or less permanently and emitting swarms from time to time (Richards and Richards, 1951). There is a dangerous period before the new workers hatch, as with single queens, for the swarm workers die off gradually and the queens are entirely dependent on them. An algebraic model constructed by the Richardses (and mentioned again later in more detail) was used to calculate the best ratio of queens/workers in the swarm, that is, the ratio that produced most queens in the ensuing interswarm period. It was assumed that if d was the time from egg to adult eggs giving queens were laid between d and $2d$. The actual values were 16 queens and 98 workers ($d = 30$ days and longevity of worker $= 45$ days), which accorded reasonably with fact. Hamilton (1964a and b) has suggested that the greater degree of pleometrosis in tropical wasps may arise from a higher population "viscosity" and a lack of synchronization of sexual production, both of which might be expected to favour inbreeding and so enlarge the degree of relationship between individuals in a society. However, many populations in temperate regions are notoriously viscous too.

Fission is common in pleometrotic ants. *Monomorium pharaonis* (L) living in buildings in Scotland produced swarms of adult and young stages ranging up to nearly 5000 individuals (Peacock *et al.*, 1950). Larvae were necessary for success. What appeared to be the severing of a link between two daughter colonies of *Iridomyrmex detectus* (Smith) has been described by Duncan-Weatherley (1953); workers from the two colonies met each morning on a common trail and formed excited groups. The division of a colony of *Formica rufa* and its territory as described by Elton (1932) was a remarkably orderly process, and involved a recognition of new boundaries without hostility. Gösswald (1951) says that several thousands of workers and about 100 queens of *F. polyctena* start new colonies. *Oecophylla* sends out swarms of several hundreds of workers (at least 600 are necessary) that settle in empty trees and yield brood in 9 days from their own eggs (Ledoux, 1950). Such all-worker groups collect queens after nuptials, for many leave the nests, even though there is evidence that they are fertilized beforehand by visiting males (Vanderplank, 1960). The situation in *Crematogaster* is similar (Soulié, 1962).

In *Eciton hamatum* Fabricius, a doryline ant that is haplometrotic, division into 2 parts follows production of a sexual brood of some thousands of males and fewer than 10 females (Schneirla, 1956; Rettenmeyer, 1963a). Queens emerge first and space themselves out, even going outside the bivouac and taking a cluster of workers with them. Division occurs when the males emerge, and as the colony has young brood, a nomadic phase is started with the old queen moving one way and the selected young queen in the opposite direction. Only 2 parts, not necessarily equal, are formed, and a connecting column persists for a day, during which time removal of one queen is followed by refusion. Fertilization takes place on the ground at a later date. It is also possible, as in *Apis mellifera*, for the old queen to be superseded. In Africa, Raignier (1959) has shown that the old queen of *Dorylus* (*Anomma*) species goes off with the bulk of the workers, while the rest stay with the male and female brood. One of these is selected. If she dies or is removed too late for reunion, the residue dies. Haplometrosis in this subfamily thus appears to be derived from controlled pleometrosis, the new queen being selected from a set of daughters. Though endogamy is possible and would raise the degree of relationship of the new workers to $\frac{3}{8}$, it seems unlikely, as males, which can fly, can approach from other colonies which, due to the seasonal nature of reproduction, would be expected to be in the air simultaneously. Nor is it necessary, for once social organization has evolved, and haplometrosis been re-established, exogamy need not lead to deterioration, as the workers are all sisters with $\frac{3}{4}$ relationship (assuming single insemination).

Termites may reproduce by fission, especially the more advanced ones. Grassé and Noirot (1951) have described "sociotomie" in which a swarm consisting apparently of all castes and ages, even winged sexuals, emerges and moves to a new site, where another colony is generated from the original couple or their substitutes. The peculiar facility with which even primitive termites replace their damaged or destroyed sexual pairs leads to a form of budding, especially seen in *Reticulitermes*, where the colony appears to have little cohesion and spreads out forming substitutes as soon as contact with the main nest is lost (in Grassé, 1949).

Meliponine bees are mainly haplometrotic and divide following a period of controlled pleometrosis. They seek a suitable nest site, often one that has earlier been inhabited, at up to several hundred metres distance (Kerr, 1951; Nogueira-Neto, 1954; Kerr and Laidlaw, 1956). Workers then fill cracks and build the entrance funnel, using materials (cerumen, pollen, honey) from the parent colony if necessary. Even cells are started. Males accompany the workers and fly round the nest entrance. Next a virgin, up to now imprisoned in wax in the parent nest, is released and flies to the new site; others may be killed. Mating probably takes place in the open, though there are no observations of this. It may be at least a week, perhaps 3, before the young queen starts laying. A record case of speed is 17 days from start to the first egg in the species *Tetragonisca jaty* F. Smith (Moure *et al.*, 1958).

Bees of the genus *Apis* are haplometrotic and well known to reproduce by division into 2 or more parts after a period of controlled pleometrosis (Ribbands, 1953; Butler, 1954a, 1958, for general comments). Recently Martin (1963) has found that colonies of more than 10^4 bees emit 2 out of 3 workers in a swarm, those of less emit 4 out of 5, and if occasionally small colonies do swarm the number left may be nonviable. The swarm must consist of at least 250 bees, otherwise they cannot form a cluster and have great difficulty in guiding themselves to a new nest site. The proportion left is increased by spacious conditions, by queen cells, and by a poor supply of queen substance. Evidently the first two restrain, and the last fails to draw out the bees. The age distribution has been known for a long time through the work of Morland, summarized by Butler (1940); and recently reinvestigated by Meyer (1956); all ages are represented, but except in swarms from crowded colonies which are random collections of bees, young and middle-aged individuals predominate, thus ensuring survival over the few weeks before new workers can be produced. Honey is carried in the bee crop. A nest site may be located before the swarm, which may, as Taranov (1947) has suggested, be differentiated much earlier, emerges (except in migratory swarms, Martin, 1963). The residue in the nest have young brood and an ample supply of young bees, but run the risk of losing their new queen when she mates, or of failing to get her mated due to bad weather in the 3 or 4 weeks during which she is receptive. Both exogamy and multiple insemination are the rule. Several queens are produced, but instead of being held in reserve until after the mating flight they are either killed in their cells by the dominant virgin or allowed to emerge one by one to contest with her (Wenner, 1964) until only a few, sometimes only one, survive. Mass emigration can be induced in *Apis mellifera* by disturbance or starvation, and it is a regular pattern of behaviour in other species of the genus. They only agree on a new site once the bees in a temporary cluster have full crops, an interesting way, perhaps, of sampling the trophic potentialities of an area (Martin, 1963).

Whereas the fission of pleometrotic colonies presents few problems of continuity, that of haplometrotic ones does. The new queen has to be brought into use in the new part as soon as it becomes independent, and this usually has to be achieved in face of the hostility of the old queen. In *Apis* the old queen leaves; in *Dorylus* (*Anomma*) the same is true and perhaps in *Eciton*. It is interesting that all these are migratory genera (*Apis mellifera* being the least migratory species), and reproduction rather resembles a partial migration in which a viable residue is left (Ribbands's theory). The emigrating part has to find a new place, make a comb and survive until new workers can be matured. The residue has to select and mate a queen exogamously, but it need make no comb and probably has a fair reserve of young brood. Both parts face rather different difficulties. If the old queen remains, as in meliponine bees, the residue risks nothing and the chances of survival of the bud depend on the care given to it.

CHAPTER 4

BROOD PERIODICITY

Of the many periodic influences on insect societies only those affecting brood will be considered here. As far as present knowledge goes, extreme fluctuation is uncommon. The periodicity that the queen starts is soon damped out in most cases, if not by the imprecision of later reactions, then by the sheer limit to oviposition rate. This is probably an advantage, provided the system governing the distribution of work is versatile enough to enable a suitable allocation of labour to the varied jobs that have to be performed. In general this appears to be true in *Apis mellifera*, which is best understood, for new workers after a short period of cell cleaning appear to disperse over the brood area and respond to the situations that require action, though their preferences change with age and vary with size (Kerr and Hebling, 1963). They show little job-fixation (Ribbands, 1953; Lindauer, 1952; Istomina-Tsvetkova, 1957, 1963), and indeed Wenner (1961) has suggested that a Markov process might make a suitable model of bee behaviour in the hive. The same applies to their foraging programme, which is both conservative and pliable (Levin, 1961; Free, 1960, 1963). This probably applies to most bees, wasps, and ants, and perhaps to termites, though in some size and in others age is the more important variable (see Wilson, 1963b; Otto, 1958a; Weir, 1958a and b). Given this degree of behavioural complexity, a steady flow of material from egg to adult, with numbers in each stage proportional to the duration of that stage, is more likely to create stable working conditions than is marked periodicity.

A. BEES AND WASPS

The overproduction of eggs and larvae by the queen of *Dolichovespula sylvestris*, inefficient in the limited context of the initial stages of this society, may well be regarded as a valuable step towards an aperiodic system. The initial periodism of *Bombus*, although it appears to be due to the release of egg laying in response to pupae reinforced by an increase in the food in circulation after completion of a batch of larvae, does tend to disappear as the colony grows, especially in the more advanced pollen storers (Cumber, 1949a). This is largely due to the variable larval period which spreads the pupae in time, to the age range of pupae used (even though young ones are preferred), and perhaps to a limited egg-production rate (A. D. Brian, 1951, 1952). In *Trigona* (*Scaptotrigona*) *postica* Latr. (Meliponidae), however, the queen oviposits periodically after some 10–20 cells have been made (Sakagami and Zucchi, 1963), feeding meanwhile on food brought for larvae and eggs laid by workers. In *Melipona compressipes manaosensis* Schwarz, on the other hand, the process proceeds one cell at a time (Sakagami and Oniki, 1963). The honey-bee *Apis mellifera*, however, is *par excellence* aperiodic, and though its brood flow varies in size seasonally and geographically, all stages are normally present at once (Bodenheimer, 1937b; Jeffree, 1956). This also applies to the primitive *Allodape* complex of bees (Sakagami, 1960; Michener, 1962), in which the founding female appears to lay slowly and continuously so that a full sequence of brood forms from egg to young adult are present at one time. Though their brood-rearing behaviour is highly complex, their sociality is weak, for Michener has only recently produced evidence that unfertilized daughters assist their mother.

B. TEMPERATE ANTS

If the life cycle is long compared with an annual climatic cycle, periodicity is inevitable. This applies to myrmecine ants in boreal zones, such as *Leptothorax* species (Headley, 1943). Eggs give rise to larvae of a certain stadium by winter and these generate pupae and adults the next season. Of course, there is considerable overlap of brood types in summer and behavioural plasticity is still essential. A variant of this is seen in *Myrmica* species (Brian, 1951, 1957b). Two synchronous peaks of eggs and pupae each year are separated by a larval peak in summer and one in winter (Fig. 1). The first egg and pupal peaks are larger than the second ones and the summer larval peak is smaller than the winter one. At first sight this association of eggs and pupae recalls *Bombus*, *Polistes*, *Vespula*, and others, but the situation is, in fact, more complex. Nor do single brood waves flowing from a periodic oviposition entirely explain the periodicity, for if so the first large egg wave would give a second large pupal wave, and the second small egg wave a first small pupal wave.

In fact, oviposition is not periodic. It rises quickly to a peak and then declines to zero about 3 times more slowly (Brian and Hibble, 1964). This applies whether the eggs are removed before they hatch or left in, that is, hatching larvae do not influence the egg-laying programme (cf. *Polistes*). The egg trough is caused by the egg-eating behaviour of first instar larvae which remain in the agglutinated egg-mass until the workers move them in the second instar (Weir, 1959). This generates an oscillation even with a constant egg-laying rate; but the actual programme of egg production accentuates the periodicity at first, but later damps it strongly, so that the second wave is much smaller than the first and a third is stopped by preparations for winter.

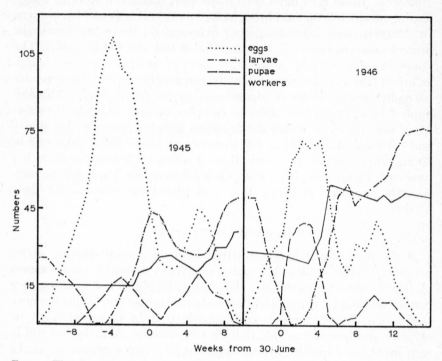

Fɪɢ. 1. The sequence of population structure for two consecutive years in a captive colony of the ant *Myrmica rubra* L. During the winter there is a small worker mortality (after Brian, 1951).

A proportion of the larvae that cut out the trough in egg frequency metamorphose immediately and form the small second pupal peak; the rest and all those from the second egg wave diapause and form the large winter larval population. But the synchronization of the small second egg and pupal peaks is due in part to the equal duration of egg, larval, and pupal stages, and in part to sharing a common terminating influence originating in the queen: concurrently with her reduced power of egg laying goes a reduced power to stimulate metamorphosis (Brian, 1963). As a result both cease, though metamorphosis is also influenced by a maternal factor transmitted to the egg, by the ageing of the workers, and by their displacement by new workers which are incapable of promoting metamorphosis (Brian, 1962), as well as by declining temperatures (Brian, 1963).

During winter the activity of the larval population as well as of the queen is regenerated and they respond together to spring warmth, though with slightly different thresholds: 7–8°C for larval growth, 9–11°C for oviposition, and 13–15°C for metamorphosis (Brian, 1957b). Winter cold thus co-ordinates queen and larval functions and one can say that control is external, whereas in autumn it is, at any rate in an immediate sense, internal. A constant incubation temperature destroys the cycle completely.

Spring release by temperature, autumn closure by a physiological cycle, and co-ordination in the intervening period by ontogenetic rate adjustment does not entirely exclude the mutual influence of brood streams. To test this possibility dephasing experiments in which the queens were incubated earlier or later than the larvae were set. It was found that the egg peak was moved correspondingly forwards or backwards and was, in fact, simply determined by the time the queen started to lay and the time larvae began to hatch, a matter solely of temperature relationships, not of the larval population. As workers take 4 weeks as compared with the queens 1 week to warm up before laying, they normally start just before her eggs are due to hatch, but a delay of several weeks gives the workers a chance to form an egg-mass of their own, and they are reluctant to accept a queen, which still further delays her egg laying. Nevertheless, very large peaks occurred in the experiment, probably mixed, but it is possible that some of the worker eggs were eaten by the queen and so converted into fertile ones (Weir, 1958a and b).

As "free" worker eggs are known to decrease with the numbers of overwintered larvae (Brian, 1953a), cultures of queens with workers and larvae in various ratios, even with larvae continuously added to saturate the workers, were set up, but still the queen produced eggs at the same time; these hatched at the same time and their numbers varied randomly, not in inverse relation to larval number (Brian, 1957b). The only factor that did affect egg number was the gross food supply, but this did not influence the timing of egg frequency.

Hence, if there is a relation between the two brood streams or subsystems (queen to eggs and larvae to pupae), it acts by influencing the survival of young larvae during the period when they compete for worker attention. Evidence for this comes from the demonstration that queen eggs diluted with worker eggs survive better, and that overwintered larvae compete lethally with young larvae hatching from current eggs, and reduce the proportion of worker-biased brood that survives (Brian, 1962). This ensures a compensatory production of larvae if the winter worker/larva ratio is above average and vice versa. The absence of a direct response by the queen to the degree of occupa-

SIP–B

tion of the workers may well be primitive and by no means characteristic of ants in general, for in this genus the queen is fairly independent and feeds herself on prey as they are being malaxated, and the use of worker eggs as a colony currency does not appear to be widespread in ants (see Brian, 1964a).

It would be interesting to know to what degree societies have been selected for programme efficiency of this sort. The egg/larval oscillation originates presumably in the claustral method of colony foundation, with the agglutinated egg-mass from which larvae are not extracted until they have eaten some younger sister eggs, and is valuable at that stage. The production of rapidly developing non-diapause brood shortens the dependent larval period and produces adults, and hence feed-back, earlier (and they live as long, Brian, 1951). Both introduce egg and pupal troughs in midsummer and winter and enable the whole worker force to concentrate on the most onerous work of rearing larvae (which is anyway about the only possible activity in spring and autumn), leaving all the minor work like egg tending, pupal care, and nest construction for other times. To perfect this arrangement some adjustment of rates of oogenesis and ontogeny would be necessary, and, in fact, since larval and pupal periods are commonly nearly equal in Hymenoptera, it might only be necessary to double the egg-incubation period. The study of comparative efficiency in brood rearing is a promising and, as yet, unexplored field.

C. TROPICAL ANTS

Most tropical rain-forest ants have aperiodic brood populations (Wilson, 1959a). The Dorylinae and certain similar Ponerinae are notable exceptions. New-world Dorylines of the genus *Eciton* have marked brood cycles lasting 6–6½ weeks and generating workers, except at the start of the dry season, when sexuals are produced (Schneirla, 1957, for summary). Otherwise there is no climatic correlation. Eggs coincide with pupae and are laid about a week before the 3-week pupal period is over, giving an overlap of some 20–25 % between successive cycles. As the majority of these are laid in 2 or 3 days, a sharp wave of eggs is started which changes into larvae shortly after the workers hatch and, after 2 weeks, into pupae. Thus, as in all the other known cases, eggs and pupae alternate with larvae. The regularity of this cycle strongly suggests that oogenesis is triggered directly or indirectly by some event in the preceding brood cycle such as pupation. As in *Bombus* and others, this needs analysis.

It is almost impossible to experiment with these ants, but Schneirla after long study has come to the conclusion that the energies devoted to larvae are deflected towards the queen when metamorphosis starts, and that the general improvement in her nutrition, the extra tactile and olfactory stimulation resulting from greater attention and so on, initiate oogenesis. He does not think the queen "perceives" a significant change in the brood state. All that natural selection has to adjust is the timing of the signal in relation to oogenesis, ovulation, and incubation so that larvae hatch more or less at the same time as new workers appear. In *Eciton* the virtues of this highly periodic system are obvious, for alternating phases of activity and quiescence are always arranged to coincide with brood condition. Nomadism is an essential part of their feeding methods, and it takes place when there are larvae needing food; otherwise the colony rests in one place.

Eciton is now known to be rather extreme in its periodicity. Two species of *Labidus* show much less synchronization of broods (Rettenmeyer, 1963a). The African *Dorylus* (*Anomma*) emigrates to new feeding areas every 20–25 days instead of having periods of nomadism (Raignier and van Boven, 1955). These movements last several days and between them the colony is sedentary. It is possible to see that the brood is largely in the late pupal stage when the colony moves, and this probably means that the queen lays her eggs immediately after the move (sometimes just before) over a period of 5 or 6 days and that these mature in about 20 days. There is thus almost the opposite programme to that of *Eciton*, for *Dorylus* (*Anomma*) is stationary during the larval phase, but moves (only briefly and only once) during the late pupal and early egg phase. Again, however, the essential fact is that the brood cycle is closely associated with the behaviour cycle and presumably provides greater instantaneous co-ordination and efficiency. It would be interesting to know whether *Apis dorsata* Fabr., which is more migratory than *A. mellifera*, is also more periodic in its brood schedule. The nearctic army ant *Neivamyrmex nigrescens* Cresson, which extends to latitude 40° in N. America, responds after hibernation to rising temperature rather than to the callow brood excitation that normally initiates nomadism in summer (Schneirla, 1963).

CHAPTER 5

AGE STRUCTURE

Since the very detailed work which Bodenheimer (1937a and b, 1958) has reported on the seasonal variation in age composition of *Apis mellifera* very little has been added to our knowledge of age structures in colonies. Talbot and Headley in their numerous counts of ant colonies already referred to in various habitats have also recorded the brood present. Brian (1951, 1957b) recorded the brood and adult population composition of a captive colony of *Myrmica rubra* (then called *M. laevinodis* Nyl.) over several seasons and much of this has already been discussed in relation to brood periodicity.

The limited capacity for work and the existence of behaviour that ensures the relatively efficient deployment of this labour was shown in *Apis mellifera* by Gontarski (1953) by varying the number of larvae given to a group of workers. If a relatively few were given they grew to a large size (up to 9 times normal), but still produced workers rather than queens. If relatively many were given, an area of contiguous ones was selected and fed normally (randomly) and the rest neglected. This area was much less than the worker force could keep warm, which suggests that in spring the brood area may not be set by temperature, but by some aspect of food processing and supply, though in spring air temperatures are probably lower than they were in Gontarski's experiment. In a complete society when the proportion of larvae falls there is likely to be a mechanism that boosts oviposition so that oversize (and in other species perhaps change of caste) is avoided, but it was not included in Gontarski's experiment. Of course, change of caste can reasonably be regarded as a second consequence of shortage of larvae, to be invoked if increased oviposition cannot be induced (as, for example, if there are too few queens), but not as a primary response.

The ratio workers/larvae in colonies of *Myrmica ruginodis macrogyna* (Brian and Brian, 1949) tends to be constant at about 0·882 (Brian, 1950) and the ratio of weight of larvae to weight of workers even more so. It appears to be both stable and optimal. It is stable, since departures from a central value tend to be compensated, for it has been shown that as in *Apis mellifera* the worker force has a limited capacity to foster larvae, and tends to give priority to those that are worker-biased so that a given set of eggs yields, as the number of workers treating it are experimentally increased, first its quota of worker-biased brood (immediately giving worker adults) and then an amount of diapause brood (that hibernates) in numerical relation to the number of nursing workers (Brian, 1953b, 1957c, 1962). The relation of survival to worker number depends presumably on the attention an individual larva can command, for they are at this stage very susceptible to diseases of various sorts if not cleaned and to starvation if not fed regularly, and, of course, to being eaten by their fellows if not removed from the egg-mass in time. Probably once they become subnormal they cease to be recognizable and are destroyed and fed to normal ones. And it has already been pointed out that if larvae are short, though the workers do not appear to be able to induce the queen to lay more, they can increase the survival of such eggs as she lays by contributing their own eggs to the egg-mass. In these ways the ratio workers/larvae will tend to constancy, and any departure will be still further compensated by larval size variation.

That the ratio tends to be optimal was shown by culturing a fixed number of hibernating larvae with various numbers of workers, and assessing progress as gain in weight. It was found that gains increased up to a limit, but according to a law of diminishing return whereby each additional worker gave less benefit the more there were already. In a non-social population an optimum might well have been expected, too many workers being disadvantageous; but in *Myrmica*, although surplus workers did struggle to get at the brood, no damage was caused and the final result was that little more food was administered by considerably more workers. It is readily seen that the best worker/larvae ratio is that which gives most larval growth for least workers. Mathematically, if

$$dy/dw = a/w$$
(y = gain per unit time, w = worker number, a = a constant)
then $y = a \log w$

and the best value of w can then be found by maximizing y^2/w and this occurs when $w = \exp. (2a^2)$. By this method a value for the optimal ratio was obtained close to the observed (Brian, 1953b).

Apart from the struggle to reach a centrally condensed brood-mass which reduces individual output the larger the population, one other cause of inefficiency is apparent (Brian, 1956a). Well-fed larvae do not emit food signals, but will accept food if pressed. This process of inspection and persuasion takes longer and involves more overlap of effort at higher worker/larva ratios.

It can be expected that societies that achieve optimal winter ratios and thereby perform more economically than others will leave more offspring and so replace less efficient ones, in so far as efficiency in this sense is compatible with the other necessary functions. Such adjustment in a society will have the effect of making the optimum into a zone of stability.

This section could legitimately go on to consider the importance of the age structure of the worker population in relation to population growth and differentiation. However, recent reviews by Wilson (1963b) and Brian (1964a) make this unnecessary.

CHAPTER 6

DYNAMICS: WORKER TURNOVER

There is a flow of individuals through insect societies. Each embryo assimilates the food brought in by the adults, grows, matures, and metamorphoses. Young and adults die at all ages.

A. EGG PRODUCTION

Both fecundity, or the egg production per life, and the factors influencing egg-laying rate are discussed here. The latter is, of course, much easier to measure as well as being extremely useful. Although it is desirable to express it in terms of the total female population, as all contribute (even though the reproductive female may alone produce the eggs), data of this kind are not often available.

1. *Bees and wasps*

The queen of *Halictus marginatus* lays up to 6 eggs unaided in the first year. After that the population roughly trebles each year and so must the queen's egg output, though, expressed per female (including non-reproductive ones) the fecundity is only 3 per year. It is not certain, but 150 eggs may be the limit for one queen (in the fourth year), for after this there is evidence that auxiliary females lay and (as they are unfertilized) produce males, so that a sex ratio of 3 : 1 males : females results. In a lifetime of 5 years a single queen might lay $1 \cdot 5 \times 10^3$, but more probably $2-3 \times 10^2$ eggs (Plateau-Quénu, 1962).

Oviposition by queen *Bombus agrorum* has been estimated by Cumber (1949a) by various methods: eggs in ovarioles, eggs in nests, numbers of pupal and pre-pupal brood and numbers of vacated cocoons. All agree in showing a steady rise during May, June, and July, to a maximum of 12 per day per queen. After this the number drops off, though workers lay as well and sexuals are produced. Male-producing eggs do, in fact, appear at about the time of maximum egg-laying rate. It has already been mentioned that *Bombus agrorum* queens lay in cells built on pupae and A. D. Brian (1951, 1952) found that the number laid on each batch of pupae was proportional to the number of pupae in the batch. In two nests of different seasons similar regression coefficients averaging $3 \cdot 16$ eggs per pupa were obtained. Egg laying may therefore be controlled by the numbers of pupae forming so that an efficient structure that does not swamp older brood with younger can be maintained. Yet there is evidence that though queens prefer young pupae they will also lay on older ones, an indication perhaps that egg production is the real limiting factor. However, as any increase in egg-laying rate without an improved structure would be unrewarded, it seems more likely that this has evolved to a limit set by the design of the nest.

The wasp habit of feeding eggs to young larvae makes fecundity difficult to measure. For *Polistes gallicus*, Deleurance (1957) cites an average of 1·8 eggs a day during the initial period before any hatch, and it appears that during this period cells (even though only cell bases) limit the eggs laid and empty cells are quickly filled. Once the larvae have hatched, however, empty cells increase in number and no new ones are made. Such priority for larval attention even in societies with workers could, by limiting the cells available, hold down oviposition to a level appropriate to the current surplus of worker power, and so maintain a controllable volume of brood flow.

Morimoto (1954c) has specially studied the rate of egg laying in *Polistes chinensis antennalis* Pérez, and found it to be independent of the number of empty cells during the pre-worker larval phase; but prior to this and again when workers have emerged there is a close connection between rates of cell construction and oviposition (as in *P. gallicus*).

Richards and Richards (1951) analysed data from 33 short-cycle polybiine nests, giving the number of queens (*q*), of workers (*p*), and of cells made per worker in a developmental period (*r*). All three were positively correlated; partial correlation eliminated all significant co-efficients except that between cell rate and queen number. This suggests that queens stimulate cell construction somehow, probably through a general activation of workers. For a 21-day period of development the number of cells per worker per day (*r*) was

$$r = 0\text{·}012\ q + 0\text{·}399.$$

The average number of workers was 132 and of queens 22, but there was considerable variation. As queens increase the number of cells, it would be expected that more eggs might be laid, too. Richards and Richards (1951) attempted to estimate this by measuring ovariole eggs, eggs in cells, and the ratio eggs/ovariole eggs. They decided that the ratio eggs in cells/number of queens gave the best estimate of current oviposition. All methods indicated an increase in the number of eggs laid with queen number, but a lower average per queen (compare Waloff's subsequent results with groups of *Lasius* queens). Again the interrelation of the queens was not known and it must not be inferred that all of them laid less than if alone. Oviposition increased with the age of the colony (for a given number of queens) and there was no evidence of a fall, as Cumber found in *Bombus*, except perhaps right at the end. Furthermore, as the colony grew the proportion eggs/total brood was fairly steady after the initial ratio of unity. This incidentally points to a lack of periodism.

Egg laying and fecundity have been extensively studied in *Apis mellifera*. Ribbands (1953) cites a maximum rate of 3×10^3 eggs a day on an empty comb and means of about 2×10^3 are recorded for a 21-day period. Bodenheimer and Ben-Nerya (1937) calculated $2 \cdot 2 \times 10^5$ in a season in Palestine. The rate rose to a peak in March and then declined almost linearly to a minimum in December. Fecundity varies with the age of the queen (either the first or second year in the queen's life is best) and with her genotype, for Cale (1952) found the F1 hybrids between inbred lines averaged 1 272–1 428 eggs a day for 46 days, whilst inbred ones gave 806–1 295. Race is also a major cause of variation in fecundity (Hassanein and Banby, 1960b).

In a young swarm the queen's laying may well be limited by the cells available as in wasps, but in an established hive with combs this is certainly not so in spring; rather the number of workers with which egg production correlates positively (Moeller, 1958) is likely to govern the area of comb that can be maintained at about 30°C and which alone is suitable for oviposition (Butler, 1954a). But food supply, particularly pollen, can be crucial in early spring, too (Farrar, 1934, 1936), and the work of Gontarski on worker/larva ratios suggests that food rather than the area heated may be limiting. As the bees increase and more combs are covered it is conceivable that given adequate food, which is, of course, converted into a highly nutritious concentrate for the queen, the colony can grow until limited by the rate at which the queen can produce eggs, for the size in early summer is certainly known to be correlated with the age and race of the queen, and Nolan (1925) showed fairly convincingly that colonies with poor queens drop behind those with good ones from May onwards. But it is perhaps more likely that space, absolutely or by virtue of a particular clustering habit, limits oviposition first. It is known that wild nests make 3, rarely 5, long broad combs when they have natural nesting holes big enough (Ribbands, 1953).

2. *Ants*

The laying power of queen ants varies enormously. The primitive myrmicine genus *Myrmica* has already been discussed from several points of view: food restriction reduces egg yield, but competition with larvae does not, except in the case of eggs laid by workers. Queens under ideal laboratory conditions with ample workers lay on an average 628 eggs in a season of 16 weeks at 20°C (Brian and Hibble, 1964).

It is not possible, in spite of Weir's comments (Weir, 1959b), to distinguish all eggs laid by workers from those laid by queens, hence Brian (1957a) only collected eggs laid before worker ovulation had started (a 3-week period at 20°C). It is quite clear from the results, however, that workers do not confer a proportional benefit: with 10 workers about 40 eggs and with 100 workers about 63 eggs were laid. In another experiment a queen with 6 workers gave 4 eggs maximum, and one with 130 workers (over 20 times as many) 24 maximum.

Most workers of *M. ruginodis* lay eggs if given both sugar and protein (Brian, 1953a). At 25°C, 3 or 4 eggs a week per worker were the maximum, but the rate fell off after a few weeks and only 16 per worker were laid in a season, an average of 1 a week.

The pleometrotic myrmicine *Monomorium pharaonis* was found by Peacock (1950) to average some 350 eggs in a lifetime or some 1·51 per day (per queen). *Formica rufa* was estimated to lay at most 300 eggs per queen per day or $6 \cdot 3 \times 10^4$ in a summer by Gösswald (1951), and the small wood ant (probably *F. polyctena*) was estimated to lay 10 eggs a day, but it is strongly pleometrotic and could easily produce more than *F. rufa*, which has only 1 or relatively few queens. The workers of *F. rufa* but not *F. polyctena* lay male-producing eggs. The doryline ants are exceptional: Schneirla (1957) estimates over 6×10^4 eggs in a single brood of *Eciton hamatum*, and over 12×10^4 for *E. burchelli* Westwood. Such brood are produced every 37 or 34 days respectively, so that the daily averages are $1 \cdot 5 \times 10^3$ and $3 \cdot 5 \times 10^3$. Raignier and van Boven (1955) estimated $3-4 \times 10^6$ eggs in a month or 1×10^5 a day for *Dorylus (Anomma) nigricans* Ill. certainly outstanding.

Termites show a general correlation between evolutionary complexity and fecundity. The relatively primitive Calotermitidae and Termopsidae show very little enlargement of the abdomen and lay, according to Grassé (1949), some $2-3 \times 10^2$ eggs a year; Rhinotermitidae are intermediate and lay some thousands of eggs a year, and amongst the Termitidae, a highly evolved family where there are, moreover, cases of extreme physogastry, Grassé records about $3 \cdot 6 \times 10^4$ eggs in a day (*Bellicositermes natalensis* Hav.).

B. SURVIVAL

Survival from the egg stage to the end of adult life is included here, though it is often convenient to consider adults separately. Loss of brood, unless it can be fed back, is a serious leak from the society and even phytophagous forms consume their own brood. Thus workers of

Apis mellifera eat eggs dropped by the queen when she cannot find a cell, and workers of some *Bombus* species eat eggs especially when the queen is removed. It is unusual to eat older brood, however, and at least *A. mellifera* commonly throw pupae that are damaged away. The cellular system of bees (and wasps) must eliminate brood eating by brood. Ants and termites are notorious consumers of all brood and adult stages.

1. Bees

Life tables have been worked out for very few species. Probably the best so far is the table of *Bombus agrorum* in two seasons (A. D. Brian, 1951, 1952). The averages for both seasons were: 71 % of eggs hatched, 73 % of larvae pupated, 90 % of pupae gave adults. Hence 34 % or 1 in 3 of the eggs gave adults. Worker longevity obtained from 39 marked individuals gave a negative exponential survival curve. Data from 48 *B. humilis* Ill. workers give a very similar curve (A. D. Brian, unpublished). These, of course, indicate a constant specific death-rate (μ), since if

$$y = a\{\exp. \ (-\mu t)\}$$
$$\text{then } y'/y = -\mu$$

This has a value around 4 % per day and gives a mean length of life $1/\mu = 25$ days and a half-life of 25 ln2 or 17·5 days. Such a survival curve implies accidental death from hazards of rain and wind and predation; in fact, in bad weather more are lost and house bees live slightly longer than foragers.

A good many eggs of *Apis mellifera* are eaten by workers as already mentioned and their viability varies with strain. Cale (1952) found that inbred strains had 47–79 % viable eggs whereas hybrids had 70–100 %. Egg viability is greatly reduced by sibling mating, most losses occurring just before hatching (Hachinohe and Jimbu, 1958). This is a strong argument against mass provisioning unless the cells are periodically opened. Survival in larval and pupal stages is high, for brood gaps are rare (see also Bodenheimer, 1958).

The longevity of adult workers is very variable, depending on season, weather, proportion foraging, colony size, brood condition, and strain (Kaschef, 1959; Hassanein and Banby, 1960a; Kapil, 1957). Recently Free and Spencer-Booth (1959) obtained a measure of seasonal variation by introducing young marked bees into a colony every week from March to October. Mean life length was 5 weeks in March and 4 in June; from August onwards they survived all winter, but did better the later they emerged in the autumn. Winter bees are probably in diapause, as they accumulate reserves in the fat body, do not develop ovaries even if the queen is removed, and their oxygen consumption is only half that of summer bees at the same temperature (Maurizio, 1946). Bodenheimer

(1958) suggests that taking into account the period in the hive when little mortality occurs the survival function (l_x) of the honey-bee is "half-normal" so that

$$l = a \, \{\exp. \, (- \, \mu x^2)\,\}$$

hence $l'/l = - \, 2\mu x$

and the specific mortality rate (μ) increases with age (x). A mean of 30 days, however, indicates an approximate daily loss of 3 % per day as in *Bombus*. This is confirmed by the work of Lundie cited in Bodenheimer (1958), which shows that about 3 % of foragers die in the field each day.

Ribbands (1953) showed that foraging was a real hazard by getting a mean longevity of $30 \cdot 1 \pm 1 \cdot 2$ days for bees which started early as compared with $37 \cdot 1 \pm 3 \cdot 6$ for late starters. However, Mauermayer (1954) failed to increase longevity by shading a colony and reducing foraging; but food may have been inadequate. Taranov (1952) found that small colonies had a lower survival and might send as much as 60 % of bees out to forage, which provides a possible explanation, though again factors such as temperature regulation could have influenced the result. Jeffree and Allen (1956) found that colony size in winter had a more complex effect on survival, for both small and large colonies lost a greater proportion of bees than medium-sized ones. The optimum November size was 11×10^3, and such a colony would be expected to lose 18 % of the bees over winter, whereas colonies of either 7 or 35×10^3 would lose 36 and 44 % respectively. Colonies with *Nosema* had a larger optimum and lost higher percentages. The authors suggest that the optimum is connected with the dynamics of heat production and consumption in clusters. It should be recalled, however, that Allen and Jeffree (1956) have found a significant negative partial correlation between colony size and brood in October and November (pollen being adjusted), which surely indicates that large colonies rear fewer brood just before winter and perhaps have older bees as a result. This is an interesting form of density-dependent mortality.

Brood rearing decreases longevity as well as reducing the fat body and the pharyngeal glands; even in autumn it decreases longevity in spring (Poteikina, 1958, 1961). It is far more important than genotype or foraging activity according to Maurizio (1961), who says that length of life is increased if pollen is available as food, especially in the first week, but only provided there is no brood to feed. Maurizio claims to have produced "winter" or "dry-season" type bees in summer by restricting brood, and though the precise mechanism is not known it seems possible that the brood stimulates endocrine activity by a neurohumoral path.

2. *Ants*

The survival of brood in a captive society of the ant *Myrmica rubra* has been measured by Brian (1951). Calculated from 2 seasons' data, the figures for larvae and pupae are reliable, but egg survival is so subject to social and trophic conditions that only a maximum is meaningful. In several cases this was in the order of 50 %, hence the survival/stage function runs: 100 eggs, 50 larvae, 42 pre-pupae, 37 pupae, and 33 worker adults, showing that about 1 egg in 3 gives a worker adult under good conditions (as with *Bombus agrorum*).

Survival in the egg and early larval stage has also been investigated experimentally. The best temperature is around 22°C (Brian, 1963) and sugar as well as protein is necessary (Brian and Brian, 1951). Survival also improves up to a limit the more workers there are (Brian, 1953b). The seasonal type of worker has little effect, even new workers being quite successful at maintaining larvae, though they cannot metamorphose any. Diapause and non-diapause biased eggs show differential survival probably in the early larval stage: thus if winter larvae persist they reduce the proportion of non-diapause brood arriving from an egg batch (as already mentioned); also, the more workers there are the more diapause-biased eggs survive though non-diapause brood is invariable (Brian, 1962).

The survival of worker-laid eggs is very variable, as they are freely eaten by the queen and fed to larvae (Brian, 1953a; Weir, 1959a). The number of such eggs first exceeded 10 when the worker/larva ratio rose to 3·3 in a variety of laboratory experiments all of which were well supplied with food. Mixed in with queen-laid ones they improve their survival (Brian, 1962), presumably by providing alternative food sources. Eggs laid by workers are, of course, haploid and male, and Brian and Carr (1960) produced evidence that random mixtures gave a higher proportion of males in bigger egg-masses (workers of constant number), which implies that in large colonies, which are likely to have bigger egg-masses than small ones, male larvae may have a better chance of survival, as well as (on account of the higher worker/queen ratio and better feeding) being more frequent. Males are under natural conditions only produced in medium and large colonies (Brian and Brian, 1951). The queen has a big influence on survival in the larval stage. In her absence workers prefer to feed big larvae and may entirely neglect small ones (Brian, 1957c; Brian and Hibble, 1963a), but if she is present the balance is tipped in favour of the small ones and large ones may even be attacked. In addition she has a general stimulatory effect on worker activity (Brian and Carr, 1960; Brian and Hibble, 1963a and b).

Some data on the longevity of workers of *Myrmica rubra* in a captive colony have been given (Brian, 1951). Age groups were marked by removal of functionless epinotal spines. Of 79 new workers, 18 (23%) died within 5 weeks of emerging. Some had obvious anatomical defects, and the rest died throughout the summer of their second year, dated from the egg stage. This, interestingly enough, was true whether they matured the same year as laid or the next year (after wintering as larvae), which implies that larvae age at the same rate as workers. This is, of course, a strong argument against retaining brood in this wholly dependent stage any longer than possible. The specific mortality rate is thus seen to be around 50% per annum.

Little exact information exists for other ant species except *Monomorium pharaonis*. Workers lived at most 9–10 weeks and queens 39 weeks (Peacock and Baxter, 1950). If a mean of 9 weeks is taken for workers, the specific mortality rate is about 2% per day, almost as high as that of *Bombus* and *Apis*.

C. IN STATIONARY POPULATIONS

It is reasonable to assume that turnover is most meaningful in stationary populations which will have life-table age distributions, in which case it can be measured as the reciprocal of the mean age at death. It is the same as the reciprocal of the half-life in symmetrical death-rate/age distributions (physiological type), and the same as the specific mortality rate if the survival function is negative exponential (and the death-rate function skew). Not enough is known about this quantity in different social insects for generalization. The evolution of caste differences probably involves a lessening of worker age as an undesirable consequence of other changes, for the only possible situations where it is desirable to reduce their longevity is if they are not adaptable enough; but there is no evidence of this.

This loss or leakage has evidently been more than compensated in many forms by queen fecundity (or pleometrosis), for in general it is the advanced societies that are largest and have most or biggest queens. In fact, as the worker becomes more worker-like the queen must become more queen-like.

A few special cases of complete flow may be considered. First *Bombus agrorum*: if 12 eggs are laid per queen per day and 34% of eggs give adults, this produces 4 adults per day at the maximum summer rate. Since the wastage of adults is 4% per day, a population of 100 could be steady. Cumber records 107 workers as a maximum for this species in August (no sexuals at this time).

Apis mellifera populations reach 6×10^4 workers in good hives in June and the wastage is 3% per day or $1\cdot8 \times 10^3$. The queen therefore needs to lay, allowing for 70% viability, some $2\cdot6 \times 10^3$ eggs each day.

This has been recorded of good queens at peak periods, though clearly very little is allowed for mortality in the larval and pupal periods.

Myrmica rubra queens under good conditions at 20 °C lay an average of 628 eggs in a year (Brian and Hibble, 1964). With 33 % survival to the adult stage and 23 % mortality of young adults before they contribute to the society, this will give about 160 workers. With 50 % wastage per annum, a population of 320 could be maintained per queen. Out of 47 nests collected only 5 exceeded this ratio workers/queen, the maximum being 556, which is quite a reasonable result.

Monomorium pharaonis may lay 1·5 eggs per day per queen (of which there may be over a hundred), and guessing that only 1 in 3 of these matures (as in *Myrmica*), then if this exactly balances a wastage of 2 % per day each queen can maintain 25 workers. This is a reasonable figure according to data in Peacock *et al.* (1950).

These are fair preliminary models. To improve on them, of course, many more data must be obtained and a model made that is subject to external and internal variation, and which allows for growth and the emission of sexuals.

CHAPTER 7

GEOMETRIC GROWTH

Once the colony is established there is normally a period of rapid growth during which the rate is proportional to the worker population. A very simple example of this is *Halictus marginatus*, which has a series of discrete generations, one a year for 5 or 6 years in succession (Plateau-Quénu, 1962). These form a geometric series with common ratio 3, so that the population (N) is given by

$$N_n = N_0 3^n, \; n \text{ being the generation.}$$

Alternatively this may be written for continuous time as

$$N_t = N_0 e^{rT}$$ with T the mean time of a generation and r the specific growth rate or innate capacity for increase. The population statistics used in this paper are defined in Andrewartha and Birch (1954). It has the value 1·1 per individual per annum (since $T = 1$ year). The net reproductive rate (R) is

$$N_T/N_{T-1} = e^r = 3.$$

From the brood details of *Bombus agrorum* given by A. D. Brian (1951, 1952) it is possible to work out R as follows. Survival from egg to pupa is 0·56 and 3·16 eggs are laid on each pupa, so that one pupa "generates" $3·16 \times 0·56 = 1·77$ pupae in the next generation. Clearly this system shortens the generation time, though it doesn't take in the whole worker-population potential. Each generation of pupae "dies" after giving rise to the next generation and though growth is geometric as in *H. marginatus* it is still of the non-recurrent type. Failure to use the whole worker force may be due, as already suggested, to the necessity to preserve a compact nest cluster which is easily warmed and protected from predators.

The time from egg to pupa (19·5 days) may be regarded as an estimate of T. This assumes that pupae are laid on as quickly as they form, which will probably not be quite the case, even though young ones are preferred. Hence r is 0·03 per individual pupa per day or 3 % per day, comparable with the rate of loss of workers. This figure is greater than that of *H. marginatus* by virtue of the shorter generation time. Survival from pupa to adult is 0·9 and after that negative exponential: 0·4 to

19·5 days of age and 0·1 to twice this time. Hence it can be shown that the adult population is:

$$N_n = \cdot 9a \left(R^n + \cdot 4R^{n-1} + \cdot 1R^{n-2} \right)$$

and if a the number of pupae that the queen makes unaided is 5, and $R = 1\cdot77$, the populations $N_3 = 32$, $N_4 = 57$ and $N_5 = 100$ are obtained, all reasonable values. The ratio of workers to pupal increment can be calculated as $1\cdot25$, and since $1\cdot37$ larvae give 1 pupa, the worker/larva ratio should be 0·91, again a reasonable figure.

The Soper-Thompson generating function (Cole, 1954) could have been used. As only one generation reproduces (as pupae in effect), $G = 1\cdot77$ T_1. But workers survive without breeding in the strict sense and it can be shown that 1 pupa is ·7 workers after 19·5 days and ·2 after twice this period; after that a negligible number survives. Hence the generating function is

$$(1 + \cdot 7T_1 + \cdot 2T_2)/(1 + 1\cdot77T_1).$$

This expands to give 1, 2·7, 5·6, 11·2, 22·4, 44·8 in successive generations if R is taken as 2 for simplicity instead of 1·77. Multiplied by the number that the queen produces alone (say 5) this gives a reasonable series and a reasonable worker/larva ratio. Cumber (1949a) found that the ratio rose to 1·0 before sexuals were produced in societies of widely differing sizes.

Richards and Richards (1951) constructed a mathematical model of the growth of societies of polybiine wasps. Many of the relevant data have already been mentioned. As there was no indication of a rise in oviposition rate the observed rise in worker/larva ratio must be due to the accumulation of workers. In the model it is assumed that rate of cell construction rather than egg supply is limiting and that cells are used repeatedly for as long as the society survives. The longevity of workers is greater than their developmental period (d) and was assumed to be less than twice this. The rate of cell construction was taken as a constant characteristic of the worker rather than as a social function. In this way an algebraic model was constructed for a $3d$ period, the normal life of "short-cycle" societies. Reasonable observed values of the parameters were then inserted and it was found that the worker/larva ratio fell during time o to d to about 0·1 and after that fluctuated between this and 0·5 approximately. On day d this ratio is independent of the numbers of founder workers, decreases with d and has a limited value as survival increases in relation to d. The number of cells is proportional to the founder workers only, and grows very quickly. The rate of gain of the natural logarithm of population in time declines slightly, but can be taken to be approximately linear, that is, growth is exponential. The innate capacity for increase, r, has the value 0·1 per unit per day, 3 times its size for *Bombus agrorum*. For these wasps $T = 53$ days (that is 30 + 45/2) whence R is 200, a very high value, perhaps explained by the tropical environment.

Lövgren (1958) has made a model of an annual wasp society. Two cases were examined: when the same cells are used for both castes of female and when different ones are used. The basic assumptions affecting early growth (from the first worker to the emission of sexuals) are that the proportion of worker cells empty at any time is constant (at about 0·2); that the number of cells a worker can build in unit time is constant; and that the attention needed to rear one worker is constant. Any number of queens can be present and egg laying is not a limiting factor, but the rate of cell construction is, for at any time the number of workers making cells is determined by the need to establish a constant ratio of empty cells to brood cells (assumption one above).

The model starts with 10–20 workers formed by the queens alone and is split into 3 parts: from the start to when the first queen-generating egg is laid, from then till the first queen hatches, and thence to the end of the season. In the first part seven basic equations are set out, including one which states that the rate of growth is proportional to the worker population and which naturally leads to an exponential solution. The rate constant depends on various parameters: the time of development of workers, the age at death of workers, the number of cells one worker can make, the number of brood one worker can mature, and the proportion of empty/total cells. This situation carries on until queens begin to emerge; but this will be considered in a later section. Using figures from Richards (1953), Lövgren calculated r as 0·046 per individual per day, a value intermediate between those for *Bombus agrorum* and for Polybiinae.

The growth of captive colonies of honey-bees has been fully discussed by Bodenheimer (1937a and b, 1958) and by Jeffree (1955, 1956), Allen and Jeffree (1956, 1957), and Jeffree and Allen (1956). During spring various colonies showed S-shaped growth curves to which Bodenheimer fitted logistic equations with considerable success. At their start these functions approximate the exponential, and the innate capacity for increase of a society of Cyprian bees can be calculated as 0·034 per individual per day, surprisingly like that of *Bombus agrorum*. The enormous rate of growth of *Apis mellifera* colonies depends on their large overwintering population, for the amount of brood in February, March, May, and June correlates positively with this (Allen and Jeffree, 1956). An estimate of R can be obtained if T is known. As 21 days is taken to develop from egg to worker, and the average length of life of a worker is 30 days, the mean interval between an egg and its progeny of eggs (taken in effect by the workers from the queen in exchange for food and attention) is $21 + 30 = 51$ days, hence $R = e^{rT} = 5.47$, a high value.

Brian (1957a) used a geometric recurrence model to describe growth of *Myrmica* colonies during the exponential phase. It has already been pointed out that two annual broods of workers arise, one in summer from current eggs (b) and one from overwintered larvae (B). Evidence from a captive colony indicated that individuals in the egg stage in year n die in year $n + 2$ whether they are from rapid or retarded brood (Brian, 1951). Hence the workers available to rear larvae in year n that had overwintered would be b_{n-1} from the second phase of the previous year, B_{n-2} from the first phase of that year $(n - 1)$, and b_{n-2} from the second phase of year $(n - 2)$; in total

$$b_{n-1} + B_{n-2} + b_{n-2}.$$

And these would rear the current season's rapid lot (b_n), too. Hence if it is assumed that one worker can produce a workers in each brood batch, then

$$B_{n-1} = a(b_{n-1} + B_{n-2} + b_{n-2}) \text{ and } b_n = B_{n-1}.$$

In terms of annual increment (y) this means that

$$y_n = a(2y_{n-1} + y_{n-2})$$

which can be solved (Brian, 1957a) to give one real root $\lambda = a \pm \sqrt{a(1 + a)}$.

An estimate of λ is the ratio of successive winter populations which in the captive colony was 1.6 giving 0.6 for a. Hence $N_n = y_0 (1.6)^n/2a$ where y_0 is the queen-produced initial increment. This model is probably better than those given earlier. More data from wild colonies are needed.

From $\lambda = 1.6$ it follows that $r = \ln \lambda = 0.47$ per worker per year or 0.0013 per day, a very low value. Since T is 1.25 years, $R = e^{rT} = 1.8$. This, of course, could be calculated directly: any worker emerging in a b batch helps in 4 successive batches and from a B batch in 2 successive batches, an average of 3; since on each occasion a worker generates 0.6 workers, it follows that in a lifetime it makes $3 \times 0.6 = 1.8$ as above. This model grows slowly. With $y_0 = 5$ it reaches 300 in years 7–8 (and emits males) and 900 after 10 years (and emits males and females).

Bodenheimer (1937a) has fitted logistic curves to Kalshoven's (1930) data on *Neotermes tectonae*. Various sizes were reached, but rather surprisingly the initial specific growth rates of the smaller colonies were greater than those of the larger; a maximum of 240 had $r = 1.66$; of

844, $r = 0.96$; and of 2 844, $r = 0.57$, so that a high specific growth rate was associated with an early small climax. The average value of r, 1·06 per individual per year or 0·0029 per day combined with some 3–5 years for the longevity of workers (Bodenheimer, 1937a) gives R a value between 20 and 30, extremely high for a low turnover.

No generalizations are possible with such meagre data. The smallest innate capacity for increase is that of *Myrmica* (0·001/unit/day), the next that of *Neotermes* and *Halictus* (both 0·003); and then, considerably larger, are *Bombus* (0·03), *Apis* (0·03) and *Vespula* (0·05); whilst the polybiine wasps stand out at 0·1. This perhaps suggests that in general ants and termites have low, bees intermediate, and wasps high rates. If the duration of a generation which is probably numerically related to the mean age at death and hence the turnover (it must be less than this, of course) is taken into account and the net reproductive rate calculated, the two tropical forms have the greatest values (polybiine wasps 200, and *Neotermes* 30) and the temperate ones are much smaller. Of these *Vespula* (10) and *Apis* (5·5) appear to differ because the former has a larger r and a larger T, and the less-advanced bees (*Halictus* 3, *Bombus* 2) come together with the ant *Myrmica* (2).

CHAPTER 8

INTRINSIC LIMITS

Colonies have characteristic, but variable, sizes, and though frequently this may be set by external conditions there is in theory at least a limit set by the internal state. One of the most obvious is the growth of the worker population to such a size that the queen can no longer lay enough eggs to maintain exponential growth. Another is her failure to control these, or more generally for the large increments of large populations to be integrated effectively. And then there may be effects stemming from overcrowding in the nest. Efficient societies would be expected to sense the approach of these situations and avoid them by reproduction or re-queening or by increasing the number of queens, but little is yet known on this subject. Hamilton (1964a and b) has qualified this by pointing out that in theory reproduction should start once the rate of manufacture of sisters has fallen to $\frac{2}{3}$ the rate of manufacture of daughters independently. This is because the relations between sisters ($\frac{3}{4}$) is reduced to that between mothers and daughters ($\frac{1}{2}$) by this fraction ($\frac{2}{3}$). Michener (1964) has discussed and illustrated the smaller brood production per individual (reproductive efficiency) of larger societies of social Hymenoptera (though the total number of immature brood rises with colony size).

A. EGG SUPPLY

There is some evidence that eggs may be limiting. In *Lasioglossum zephyrum* eggs were apparently too few for the available pollen late though not early in the season (Batra, 1964). In *Apis mellifera* it is common knowledge that the strain and age of the queen influences the size of a colony. Moreover, Nolan, as already mentioned, has shown that although the worker population size is vital in spring (in providing a cluster temperature or a food supply) in summer egg production is limiting, and recently bee management has aimed at including several queens in a single hive. A steady seasonal decline in egg rate could account for the observed seasonal population changes in *Apis* where a peak is commonly reached in early summer, but not held even for a month (Jeffree, 1955). Although this might result from some change in behaviour in response to peak densities, it could equally well be explained by a continuously falling specific growth rate. Thus whereas in exponential growth

$$N'/N = r \qquad \text{in this case perhaps}$$
$$N'/N = a - bt^c \qquad (0 < c < 1)$$

(a, b, and c constants, t time). This species usually though not invariably replaces ageing queens (as also damaged or tethered, but not infertile ones) according to Butler (1957), but termites of the family Caloter-mitidae do not, and the colony dies out as egg production declines, even though they can and do replace damaged or dead queens (Grassé, 1949).

There are also a few cases in which sexual production anticipates the queen's decline in fecundity. In *Bombus* the queen is laying maximally (Cumber, 1949a) and polybiine wasps also give no sign whatsoever of decline (Richards and Richards, 1951).

B. NEST SIZE

Nest size both limits space absolutely and affects relative dimensions. The most well-known case is the surface/volume ratio which influences gaseous and thermal diffusion.

1. *Temperature*

Metabolic heat undoubtedly accumulates more in bigger nests and might result in superoptimal temperatures, especially in annual nests in temperate regions, when nest growth and climate both tend to raise temperature simultaneously. Many species, of course, have mechanisms of regulation and can dispose of surplus heat by ventilation, individual dispersion, evaporation of water, removal of lagging, and so on. Species of *Polybia* that range from the subtropics to equatorial regions tend to make bigger nests and store more honey in the cooler parts of their range (Richards, 1953), and species of *Polistes* tend to have larger colonies the farther north they get. This perhaps enables the advantages of haplometrosis (which is also more common to the north) such as the evolution of ferocity and caste differentiation, both of which make large size a possibility, to be fully exploited (Hamilton 1964a and b).

Apart, of course, from its lethal potentiality, temperature can have more subtle effects. Spermatogenesis, fertilization (and hence in Hymen-optera, sex), larval development (and hence caste) are all known to be critically influenced by temperature (reviewed Brian, 1964a).

2. *Chemicals*

Metabolic wastes of solid or liquid are normally carried away or covered up. Nevertheless there are imperfections and many wasps, for example, use their cells only a few times. Commensals play an important part in this process in many social insects (see Pohl, 1957; LeMasne, 1961a and b; Rettenmeyer, 1962, 1963a and b, for recent comments). Bacteriocides may also be dispersed (Lavie, 1960). The main gaseous waste is carbon dioxide, which diffuses away adequately in small nests above ground, and in larger nests its dispersal is no doubt helped by ventilation, either by active wing movements (as in bees) or perhaps by thermal convection currents such as Lüscher (1956) has suggested are generated in *Macrotermes natalensis* Haviland. The large underground nests of *Apicotermes* which often occur in waterlogged zones have a remarkable pore structure which may facilitate gaseous exchange (Weesner, 1960; Schmidt, 1960). Carbon dioxide has various physiological effects well below narcotic concentration, particularly on the behaviour of queens and workers, which has been studied in *Apis mellifera* (Ribbands, 1953), and in the ant *Myrmica* (Weir, 1957). At low concentration (4%) it is attractive (Wilson, 1962d), and in colonies of *Apis mellifera* in winter it may rise to 4% and favour successful hibernation (Taranov and Mikhailov, 1960; Mikhailov and Taranov, 1961).

Lastly there is the class of short chain carbon compounds often related to terpenes that are used in communication and which ideally should be quickly eliminated (reviewed Wilson, 1963b; Maschwitz, 1964). Wilson and Bossert (1963) have pointed out that substances of this sort, like carbon dioxide, that attract at low concentrations may release aggressive behaviour at higher ones. It is a matter of common observation that large colonies of social insects are more aggressive than small ones of the same species.

3. *Space*

The size to which nests grow must be limited by the material of which they are made and the architectural skill of the builders. This may restrict the growth of the society and cause high densities which by neurohumoral influences induce changes in behaviour that reduce population growth or initiate reproduction. Even if overdensity is temporary, as when a brood batch emerges before extra accommodation is available, it might trigger important irreversible reactions. Also density may be felt most by the traffic through constrictions like the nest entrance. Little is known about this except in *A. mellifera*, where congestion causes close-packed orientation of workers, reduces mobility and ultimately induces swarming (Simpson and Riedel, 1963).

An early example of the limited growth of a nest that doesn't appear to be due to external constraint was given by Bitancourt (1941). He showed that a nest of *Atta sexdens* L. increased its crater number logistically, reaching a maximum in 28 months and emitting sexuals, though the rate of growth had fallen off for some 6 months before this.

Mound-building by ants shows grades of success in a single genus. *Lasius* is a good example: *L. alienus* excavates its nest in soil and throws the loose material away, forming craters; *L. niger* forms mounds of excavated soil in which it sometimes excavates chambers; *L. flavus* builds structured nests with the soil it excavates and these support vegetation which helps to bind and stabilize them. Nevertheless they are limited, for Waloff and Blackith (1962) found that over 7 years the growth of small nests in max-diameter or height increased linearly and was accompanied by a change in ground plan from circular to ovoid. The size and shape varies a good deal with slope, drainage, and soil structure. It was also noted that the size did not correlate with the nearest neighbour distance. This is particularly interesting in view of the fact that Pontin (1961b, 1963; Odum and Pontin, 1961) found that the number of young queens emitted was so correlated, for the two together indicate that mound size limits population growth and leads to the emission of sexuals. More sexuals are emitted from bigger territories, presumably because more food is available for conversion.

Sands (1961) measured the diameters of mounds of species of *Trinervitermes*. The frequency distribution of 943 mounds of *T. ebenerianus* Sjöstedt was asymmetrical and appeared to be compounded of 3 or 4 different normal distributions which probably represent annual increments. After 3–4 years, growth was much slower and more often confined to supplementary nests, of which each colony had 3–6. *Cubitermes fungifaber* Sjöst. builds columns more or less contiguous as its nest grows. Each column may have one or more caps as well, so that the building is made sectionally (Noirot and Noirot-Timothee, 1962). Ants make supplementary nests connected by galleries as well: in *Lasius minutus* Emery some 4–5 (Kannowski, 1959a) and in *Formica polyctena* as many as 65 are recorded (Raignier, 1948).

Nest building in a confined space has recently been studied by Sakagami and Hayashida (1962), somewhat on the lines pioneered by Chen (1937a and b). Different numbers of workers were allowed to excavate soil packed into one end of a tube and the amount moved measured after a fixed time. Slave-makers and slaves were tested. *Formica fusca*, a slave species, showed a declining individual output as density rose and lacked even a social stimulation of 2 as compared with 1 worker (as Chen found). The slave-making *Polyergus samurai* Yano was unable to work at all and neither stimulated nor reduced the output of *F. fusca*. *Formica sanguinea* Latr., a less specialized slave-maker, could work by themselves, though they were less effective than *F. fusca* and their rate declined more with density. In both the *Formica* species the number of idle workers increased with density, but more *F. fusca* worked at higher densities than *F. sanguinea*.

This combined with higher individual output and a system of relaying soil particles made *F. fusca* a much superior worker. The authors, following Combes (1937), refer to these workers as *élites*; they are presumably workers of above average activity, able to work at above average densities (compare Wallis, 1963). However, in a limited space there is an optimum density of work and for some to stand aside rather than interfere is also valuable. The theory of this is considered in the next section.

4. *Structure*

Changes in the shape and structure of the nest as it grows may be very important, for it forms the structural framework in or on which the life processes are accomplished. Thus, clusters like those of *Bombus* that grow roughly as the surface of a hemisphere may well not allow population growth to be exponential for any length of time. In cases of this type whereas the specific growth rate of the population is a constant ($N'/N = a$) the specific growth rate of the volume is inversely proportional to its cube root ($v'/v = cv^{-1/3}$), that is, it declines as the nest grows. A tier structure in a hollow sphere improves the spatial distribution provided there are at least five tiers; but even so many wasps which build a spherical nest, with envelopes, are limited in growth rate by the speed with which they can build more layers on to the surface and remove inside ones.

Wasps, of course, show a great variety of nest design (see Grassé, 1949; Richards and Richards, 1951), ranging from the sleeve types with combs fixed to the walls, that can only be extended at the distal end, to the spherical types with freely hanging, horizontal combs that can be expanded without changing the shape. And two genera make vertical sessile combs and build cells on both sides, which both makes better use of the interior nest space and gives a more thorough ventilation with less stagnant air pockets. The form of the group, a solid catena, is readily maintained as the nest grows by adding new combs at the side as well as extending the old.

Stages in the evolution of bee nests have recently been reviewed by Kerr and Laidlaw (1956). In all cases honey is stored separately at the periphery of the brood, often in old cocoons. Primitively, in *Bombus*, pockets of pollen are built, around which a brood group clusters, and the cells are primed with pollen (Sladen, 1912). *B. agrorum* is of this type and it is striking how much better nourished the central larvae are than the outer ones (Cumber, 1949a). A further stage can be represented by those species that store pollen in separate cells, do not prime at all, and inject a paste of pollen and honey into brood cells each of which may have at first several but later only one larva (Free and Butler, 1959). In various species of *Trigona* cell clusters are developed in which each cell has only one egg; pollen may be stored in special or honey-type cells. After this the individual cells are built in horizontal strata or combs and an involucrum is formed. This is the typical meliponid type. A further step is to make vertical double-sided combs from the top downwards, though the queen still lays horizontally, crossing from one comb to another to do this. This design, which, as already mentioned, conserves space and improves air circulation, may have evolved independently from the cluster stage. It is, of course, characteristic of *Apis* species, though only *A. mellifera* has several in parallel. Hence all stages of evolution of an efficient nest structure can be traced in bees: from many brood in a cell to single brood in a cell, from clustered cells to cells stratified horizontally and finally vertically, and to double-sided combs. Such evolution confirms what is intuitively clear, that functional differentiation of design or order improves efficiency. Nevertheless even in *Apis mellifera* food is distributed randomly not evenly (to the larvae selected for feeding), the mean quantity received by a larva being proportional to the worker/larva ratio (Gontarski, 1953).

Ants and termites, as is well known, have evolved structures of linked chambers each of which houses many juveniles. These have nevertheless undergone considerable functional specialization, especially in termites (reviewed Weesner, 1960), which have special chambers for the royal couple, for fungus combs, for brood, for ventilation, for insulation, and even special capping structures (*Cubitermes fungifaber*, discussed by Noirot and Noirot-Timothee, 1962). Other structures of uncertain function exist. Even structurally unspecialized ant nests show temporary differentiation into chambers with small or large larvae, pupae, eggs, queens, and so on.

The importance of this chambered sponge form has been shown by some work with simple undifferentiated nests of *Myrmica*. On a plane they pile their larvae into a single group. Though the pile is turned quite a lot, food is not as well distributed as if the group is split into 10 small groups, which makes the larvae more accessible. The greater accessibility, however, enables the workers (when no queen is present) to express their preference for large larvae (Brian, 1956a). In angular structures workers put larvae in corners and over walls as well as on the floor, and they may stand on the roof and hold them. They spread them out through several chambers, but always adjacent ones, and so retain a massed group which nevertheless allows workers better access.

CHAPTER 9

MATURATION

Maturation is a set of changes that make reproduction possible. This chapter is concerned less with exactly what these are (this has been reviewed recently by Brian, 1964a) than with the problem of whether they respond to or anticipate a deterioration in the internal environment. First, some of the models that have been prepared are reviewed, then some actual instances examined.

A. MODELS

Lövgren's model of an annual wasp colony can be used to ascertain the best time in the summer to start making sexuals. It contains an equation relating the queens produced by the end of the season to the date on which the first queen-generating eggs are laid, and includes as a major variable the ratio of worker to queen-giving eggs laid from that time onwards (designated β). A canonical set of equations was enumerated electronically using reasonable parameters (chiefly, 150 days' season and 30 days' development period, for all adults). In the present connection the most interesting feature is that Lövgren found that if very few worker eggs were laid after queen ones had been started (β small) the time of changeover from one to the other had to be very precisely set, otherwise enough workers would not survive to rear the queens. With $\beta = 5$, the first queen eggs after 90 days, and a period of 150 days Lövgren got 15 768 cells, 3 474 workers, and 671 queens produced altogether. The ratio workers/larvae was constant for 120 days and then fell at a retarding rate. The growth curve was exponential and even the emission of sexuals did not make it sigmoid. Special cells for queens made earlier starting an advantage, but no major difference.

Unfortunately, two basic assumptions in the model are now regarded as incorrect: first, caste is trophogenically determined (see Deleurance, 1950) and it is normal for sexual production to supersede worker production entirely, once it has started ($\beta = 0$); and second, the longevity of workers must be greater than Lövgren supposed (he based his figures on *Apis mellifera*).

Richards and Richards (1951) used their model of short-cycle Polybiinae to calculate the ratio queens/workers in the early stages of the colony that led to a maximum later production of queens. They measured efficiency as the number of queens produced/old queen/day (H). The fact that the rate of cell construction is increased by additional queens was included in the model; and also that $p + 2q = 130$ (where p = number of workers and q = number of queens). If the queen-forming eggs were laid between d and $2d$ (d is the developmental period), it appeared that the best initial ratio was 16 queens to 98 workers. H varied from 0·093 to 0·159 queens/queen/day depending on the assumptions made about d and longevity. This is about 3 queens/queen/lifetime, and agrees quite well with observation. Large groups were relatively more efficient than small ones, but, of course, dispersion is better served by forming several small groups.

A general model (based on Hymenoptera, but applicable to termites) that shows the best population size or worker/queen ratio for sexual emission may be briefly discussed. It is concerned with adults only and assumes a specific rate of production that declines as the population grows, whilst the specific death rate is constant. It is also assumed that the number of mother queens is constant; then if N is the population of workers and N' the infinitesimal rate of change of this:

$$N' = \beta N^s - \mu N \qquad (s < 1)$$

(β and μ birth and death rates respectively). It is further assumed on very strong evidence that sexual production (young females in this case, as males can conveniently be neglected) is proportional to the worker/larva ratio, which is $N/\beta N^s = \alpha N^{1-s}$, and which it may be noted increases with the population size (or worker/queen ratio) up to a limit. The model can be simplified a great deal without losing its utility by making $s = 0·5$. It then reduces to

$$N' = (\beta - \alpha) N^{0·5} \qquad - \mu N$$

and integrates to
$$N = \frac{(\beta - \alpha)^2}{\mu^2} \left[1 - e^{\frac{-\mu t}{2}} \right]^2.$$

This, starting at $N = 0$ and $t = 0$, rises sigmoidally to a limit as t gets large, which has the value outside the bracket. The queens produced $\alpha N^{0·5}$ will, of course, be most when N has this value. Their number will be $\alpha(\beta - \alpha)/\mu$. One may next consider what relative values of α and β (the proportion of queens to workers produced) give the greatest queen emission rate. This can be found to be $\alpha = \beta/2$ in the special case ($s = 0·5$) considered, which means that half as many queens as workers are formed. The maximum population of workers is then

$$N = \beta^2/4\mu^2 \qquad \text{which is } \tfrac{1}{4} \text{ the size if no}$$

queens are produced ($\alpha = 0$) and the size at which such a population grows fastest.

Similar models that include juvenile stages can be made on a time base of discrete intervals. A canonical representation of the type

$$i' = aw^s - bw \qquad s < 1$$
$$j' = bw$$
$$w' = ci + ci_1 \qquad c < 1$$
$$q' = cj$$

is generally useful. Here i is the number of juveniles giving workers in the next time interval, j is the number giving sexuals, w is the number of workers, q the number of sexuals, and w' and q' the number of these at the next time unit; a, b, c, and s are constants. The behaviour of the model varies as these constants are changed, but in general the number of workers increases at first slowly at a rate governed largely by a and s, then more quickly (Fig. 2). It then slows off and may collapse to zero with the emission of numerous sexuals (b large), or oscillate before

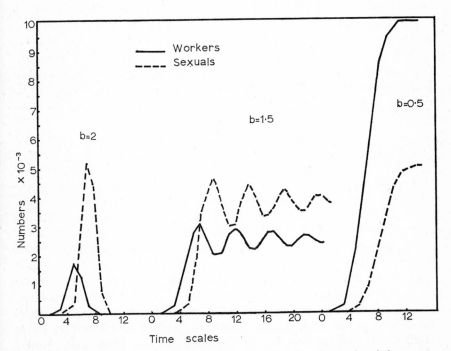

FIG. 2. Model population growth (numbers of workers) and sexual-emission rates; all constants are fixed except b, the reproductive coefficient. As this is decreased the population programme changes from an explosive type to one with an oscillatory approach to a steady state and finally to one with a gradual approach to a steady state (full details in text).

settling to a stable stationary value during which sexuals are emitted in a similar sequence 2 units of time later (*b* moderate) or approach a steady state gradually and aperiodically emitting sexuals concurrently (*b* small). If *s* is taken to be $\frac{1}{2}$, there are $(2ac/1 + 2bc)^2$ workers at equilibrium and the period of oscillation if it occurs is 5 (this being in general the number of age groups in the worker population plus 3). Maximum persistent sexual production occurs with $b = \frac{1}{2}$, and in this case the approach to equilibrium is gradual and aperiodic. Big increases in *a* which cause large rises in the steady worker population (which is a^2 if $c = 1$, its maximum value) are only accompanied by small increases in the time taken to reach this state.

Queen emission can then be regarded as a device for preventing a society growing to a size that introduces internal inefficiencies, a device that enables it to function at its best all the time. In theory it could be achieved by setting the caste-determination mechanism's response to the worker/larva ratio appropriately (varying α). As queens are likely to be more useful as propagates if stored and released periodically in masses, some at least of the disadvantages of overpopulation may have to be endured at least for short periods. Colonies that swarm will have to build up a viable swarm before emitting it, and so they, too, will not be able to avoid some overpopulation. They might grow to twice the optimum and then divide into 2, but the stage at which the sexual component is started will probably depend on rates of development in relation to population growth.

B. OBSERVATIONS

1. *Explosive types*

Halictus marginatus changes suddenly from worker to sexual production, giving 3 males to 1 female (Plateau-Quénu, 1962). This happens over several years and Lövgren's model applies only in so far as the "season" is equivalent to the queen's life. Worker production increases geometrically and would if it continued lead to $3 \times 243 = 729$ in the next generation. However, only an average of 279 sexuals mature. Since each is no bigger than a worker, this fall in worker/larva ratio seems to be unnecessary from a strictly economic point of view; moreover, Plateau-Quénu has shown that caste is determined much later, after the individual has become adult; and also, of course, the male-yielding eggs are laid, much earlier, in the previous summer. Brian (1964a) has pointed out that all the circumstances could arise from a failure of worker control by the queen and an inability to imprint worker behaviour on the new females. This might be due either to her age or to density-induced deterioration or some other intranidal change.

In *Bombus*, of temperate and especially arctic regions, the applicability of Lövgren's model may be considerable; not, probably, in direct relation to the climatic season but rather in relation to the ageing of the queen or to the flowering season. Cumber (1949a) found no evidence of a decline in queen oviposition at the time sexuals are emitted: indeed, it appears to occur at the climax, as theory suggests it should. Though the worker/larva ratio increases gradually during the season and is normally over unity when sexuals are produced, there is not a gradual rise in the female size but a sudden jump, and at the same time a sharp rise in worker/larva ratio due at least in some species to egg destruction by workers. These changes are irreversible and complete and afterwards no more workers are produced, so that the colony disintegrates. Colonies vary in size a good deal when this happens: from 30–150 workers in the case of *Bombus agrorum*, according to Cumber (1953). The cause is unknown, but the queen's governing action over worker behaviour appears to decline with age and is finally destroyed perhaps by deteriorating intranidal conditions such as worker density and higher temperatures, which increase ovary development (in queenless groups) and aggressivity (Free, 1955, 1957).

Lövgren's model is, of course, very relevant to *Vespula* species, though direct tests of the kind suggested by the author do not seem to have been carried out. According to Kemper and Döhring (1961), queens appear in *Paravespula* species about mid-September and could therefore be initiated about a month earlier. If the season lasts the five months from June to October inclusive (Lövgren's 150 days), this means that queens are initiated half-way, some 15 days earlier than he predicted. It is interesting, however, that the hypothetical growth curve for *Paravespula* which Kemper and Döhring give shows a maximum growth rate in mid-August, again as would be expected theoretically if societies are designed to produce as many sexuals as possible. The population declines a month later when gynes are produced, which could well be due to no more worker-producing eggs being laid; certainly the formation of special sexual brood cells is irreversible. Presumably, as already suggested, Lövgren's model could be very useful if the figure for survival of workers was increased.

As in the genus *Bombus*, there are forms that finish their season earlier. Four species of *Dolichovespula*, a group having smaller colonies, emit sexuals at least a month earlier and terminate correspondingly soon. The reasons for this are not known.

2. *Stable types*

These continue to produce workers after maturity. The ant *Myrmica ruginodis macrogyna* shows a gradual increase in worker size from young societies up to those of about 300 adults (Brian, 1957a). Larger societies show no further increase in size, but emit first males and then both sexes. Mature societies vary in size from about 900 to nearly 3000 workers, but it is uncertain whether they grow after emitting sexuals or simply mature at a wide range of sizes; both are probable.

The significance of the change in worker size is interesting. Very small workers are common in the early stages of societies of higher ants, and there is little doubt that they improve the chances of success in claustral foundation. In some ants small eggs are the cause (e.g. Goetsch, 1939), but in *Myrmica* this is not so, for the eggs can be transplanted into big worker groups to give normal-sized workers. The first eggs of young queens are, however, endowed with an ability to metamorphose readily at a small size (Brian and Hibble, 1964), and it is probably this, combined with a general shortage of food from the queen and her tendency to distribute it to a number of larvae, that leads to dwarf workers.

The gain in average size of worker is not, of course, due to an improved food supply, for though more food must be gathered it should theoretically be possible to distribute it equally well (to the queen to produce the eggs and then to the young larvae to produce a greater number of equally dwarf workers). Some of the gain in size may thus be due to errors in distribution or inadequate dispersal such as have already been discussed, which may be expected to increase as the colony grows and the worker/queen ratio increases, even though it is known that older queens have more power to prevent this and more power to induce early metamorphosis than young ones (Brian and Hibble, 1964). Other and important factors contribute to this situation. First, the queen's output of worker-biased eggs declines to near zero as she ages, and instead eggs are laid that tend to diapause and grow into queens, but of which many become large workers. Second, the selective survival of such diapause-biased eggs increases as the worker population grows (Brian, 1962). These two together mean more queen-potential larvae and more large workers that are "failed" queens.

Once full worker-size is reached these processes do not stop, though as there is a gap in size between the largest worker and the smallest queen there is a period in colony growth when only big workers and males appear. Males can and normally may be derived from worker-laid haploid eggs, whose best chances of survival occur when female brood is relatively scarce and when egg-masses are large, as already stated.

In the fully mature stage population ranges from 900 to some 3000 workers. Analysis of a number of mature colonies of *Myrmica ruginodis macrogyna* during hibernation, when all brood is in the last instar (Brian, 1950), showed that average larval size did not regress on colony size, which since large winter larvae are queen potential (Brian, 1954) indicates that colonies either grow after they have matured or reach maturity at a wide range of sizes. Though it was not appreciated at the time, it has since been discovered that the variation in the number of queens probably explains a lot of this variation in colony size at maturity. Thus the worker/queen ratio in 8 nests that had 1 or more queens (maximum 6) regressed positively with average larval weight ($P < 0.001$), which implies that colonies with high ratios showed more tendency to form queens than others and hence colonies with more queens must grow to a greater size than others before they mature. In fact, the worker/queen ratio would appear to have to be at least 10^3.

Two other factors correlated with larval size: worker size and worker/larva ratio. The first of these, since it has been shown that large winter larvae that fail to grow into queens give large workers (Brian and Brian, 1951), is presumably due to the large larvae produced at high worker/queen ratios—a simple causal sequence. The second (worker/larva ratio) correlated highly with larval size if worker size was held statistically at its mean (partial correlation) and has an obvious explanation in terms of the attention a larva can obtain. It did not correlate with colony size as might reasonably be expected if queens were relatively few and hence brood inadequately produced. Theoretically it would be expected to rise with the worker/queen ratio as the stable age distribution of a growing population changed into the life-table one of a stationary population as it did in the model just discussed, but this could well be obscured by a variety of internal and external disturbances. It is not surprising therefore that the worker/larva ratio appears to act on larval size independently of both worker size and the worker/queen ratio. High worker/larva ratios attained through a gradual change in proportions of brood and adults in the colony, though necessary for queen production, are secondary to the absence of the queen's inhibitory influence, for if this is lacking much of the smaller larval brood is totally neglected anyway and a high worker/larva ratio quickly established. It is believed that the subspecies studied (*M. ruginodis macrogyna*) is not secondarily pleometrotic (Brian and Brian, 1949), so that the number of queens that associate together at first will limit the final size of the colony, but species with secondary pleometrosis like *Myrmica rubra* probably only take queens in periodically, after having formed them, and then pass through a phase of worker production and growth, culminating through loss of queens in automatic renewal of the cycle. Such colonies undoubtedly kill a large number of auxiliary queens as well.

In *Formica rufa* and allied species (Gösswald, 1955; Gösswald and Bier, 1953a and b, 1954a and b, 1957) it has been shown that maturity is very much influenced by the worker/queen ratio, for the mother queens can inhibit queen formation except when the number of workers is very large: larger for *F. rufa* than for *F. polyctena*, a species having more, smaller queens. Their inhibition is seasonal, however, for after laying eggs on the surface in the spring, they descend lower in the nest, so removing, it is thought, their inhibition from the first larvae and contributing to their sexualization, though other factors such as maternal influence on the egg and the type of nurses are also involved. The temperature element in maturation has already been mentioned: in spring, when environmental temperatures are low, large nests can build up higher temperatures than small ones, and this helps the first eggs, which, unlike later summer eggs, are queen potential, to become fertilized and form queens rather than males. Scherba (1963) in a study of the mound nests of *Formica opaciventris* found that colonies that emitted female sexuals one year did not necessarily do so in other years though they might emit males, and though climate might well be involved there is some evidence of periodicity. Tolerant phases for the reception of new queens have been reported for *Formica polyctena*, but these are in winter and early spring rather than after a perennial cycle (E. T. G. Elton, 1958). Ayre (1960) did an experiment with *F. polyctena* that suggested that too big a food supply inhibited sexual production. Groups of 3000 workers and 1 queen were given 0, 50, 100 . . . 1600 mg of fly larvae a day (and diluted honeydew honey): 200 mg of this was needed to balance the population, but 400 gave more sexuals than 800 or 1600 mg. This should be confirmed, for it implies that colonies may grow to a size proportional to their food income before maturing, a situation not uncommon in other organisms with a large potentiality for size variation. No evidence of this has been found in *Myrmica*, where it is well established that lack of protein can prevent sexualization (Brian, 1964a).

Talbot (1951) found that *Aphaenogaster rudis* yielded sexuals from colonies of varying sizes not only the largest, and in *Leptothorax curvispinosus* sexual nests had rather more workers on the average (Talbot, 1957a). Colonies of *Oecophylla longinoda* mature in about 2 years (Vanderplank, 1960), and only those of more than 15 leaf nests produce buds (Ledoux, 1950). Large artificial colonies of *Monomorium pharaonis* suddenly show excitement and move out their brood; subculturing quietens them (Peacock, 1950). Maturation of termite societies also depends on their size (see Lüscher, 1961). Colonies of *Calotermes flavicollis* collected in spring yielded sexuals from their pseudergates only if some hundred or more individuals were present. If pseudergates from large colonies are split into small groups after collection, only a few of the first to moult form nymphs. The rest moult without change. As Lüscher points out, this is not necessarily a matter of dilution of an inhibitory hormone: food supply is affected by group size. Removal of the inhibition normally gives apterous sexuals even in pairs of individuals (Grassé and Noirot, 1960), and there is no doubt that low winter temperatures must play a part in the formation of fully winged individuals.

Maturity in *Apis mellifera* is still imperfectly understood, though a lot of progress has been made in the last decade. Simpson (1957, 1958, 1959, 1960; Simpson and Riedel, 1963; Simpson, Riedel and Inge, 1964) maintains that no single explanation is satisfactory, but that a variety of causes contribute. Though size is very variable, large colonies that are growing rather than declining swarm more than others, and three times as many swarms come from colonies with queens that have overwintered twice rather than once, and very few from unwintered queens. Again then, size, rate of growth, and queen age are important, but external conditions modify the time, so that early summer when food is abundant is most likely. Annual physiological cycles may be influential, too. Three main theories have been advanced (see Ribbands, 1953; Butler, 1954a, 1958): brood food, congestion, and queen control. The first supposes that surplus food follows the appearance of young workers and that this is distributed to larvae that become queens as a result; as envisaged by Lindauer (1961), it is an inability of the foragers to pass on their loads. This seems to have little factual support, and Simpson failed to induce swarming by raising the worker/larva ratio. Crowding was more successful, but not always so (Simpson and Riedel, 1963), and is certainly not a necessary condition. Woods (1959) has claimed that 25 days before swarming a decline in rate of egg laying by the queen is associated with a warble of 225–285 c/s. That the queen at least controls an early step in reproduction, queen-cell formation, is now well established (see Butler, 1963). She passes two reinforcing chemicals, one highly volatile and one hardly so, to the workers that inhibit a tendency to make queen cells. To some extent, the simple dilution of these as the society grows may lead to the first stages of reproduction, for Butler was able to show that the weaker the inhibition the more queen cells are made, and he has pointed out that fewer queen cells are made on the whole during supersedure, in which the old queen, though feebly inhibitory, nevertheless persists during the manufacture of her successor. But intranidal changes such as congestion and its side-effects may well react on the queen and interfere with the production and distribution of the inhibitors, or even with the queen's mobility, for Butler (1957) has shown that tethering queens frequently leads to queen-cell production, and Montagner (1962) that workers rear larvae less effectively the farther they are from the queen in semi-partitioned colonies. Curiously, a queen that lays no eggs at all or infertile ones may be able to prevent queen-cell formation, presumably through a dissociation of the control over reproductive and mandibular glands. Swarmed queens (from uncrowded hives) lack inhibitory power, but it is not known exactly how and when this decline occurs or what influences it; after swarming they recover quickly (Butler, 1954a, 1956, 1958, 1963).

In *Eciton* (Dorylinae) division is closely linked with season: dry in *E. hamatum* and *E. burchelli*, wet for others (Rettenmeyer, 1963a), but in *Dorylus* (*Anomma*) *nigricans* the seasonal periodicity is less marked (Raignier and van Boven, 1955). Not all *Eciton* colonies divide each year, perhaps on account of a maturation period. Schneirla has shown that *Eciton* workers separate the queen from the brood only a few of which are females, and only one of which is selected to queen the new part. It is not known why there should be so few females and so many males; Flanders has suggested that the queen is temporarily subnormal and cannot release the necessary sperm, and Brian (1958) that there is much more female mortality than usual (as in many other social insects). However, it is clear that some social state combines with a climatic change to alter queen physiology and worker behaviour.

CHAPTER 10

DYNAMICS: QUEEN TURNOVER

Societies that requeen are potentially immortal; others are not, but as the nest site may be quickly recolonized a semblance of immortality may be given. Here the number of queens or buds produced and their survival as independent colonies is considered from a simple quantitative point of view. The factors influencing their survival are the subject of later sections.

A. PRODUCTIVITY

The Richards' measure of productivity or efficiency of an established colony (H) summed over a normal lifetime will be symbolized G. Both are empirical measures and take no account of the queens that fail. This the net reproductive rate (R) does. Since in the long run R for most species is in the order of unity, they differ only in turnover. From the definition,

$$R = \int_0^\infty p_x\, m_x\ \mathrm{dx}$$

this means that either p_x or m_x may be large enough to bring R to unity. In other words the reproductive energies of a species are either directed to producing many unprotected (m large) or few protected propagation units (p large). In general the more advanced the society the greater the tendency to protection and so to low turnover.

Data on sexual production are quite common for bees and wasps, but not for ants and termites. For *Halictus marginatus*, Plateau-Quénu (1962) found an average of 279 sexuals in ratio 3 male : 1 female, giving $G = 70$ and $H = 14$/queen/year or 0·04/day (allowing a 5-year life cycle). Three nests of *Bombus agrorum* collected by Cumber (1949a) averaged 97 young queens and one of *B. lucorum* L. 83, which are in this case the H values per year (about 0·25/queen/day). There is a record of a *Bombus* in the tropics producing 450 young queens, that is 1·23/queen/day (Von Ihering quoted Bodenheimer, 1937a).

Vespula wasps (Weyrauch, 1935, according to Richards and Richards, 1951) give for three species of *Dolichovespula* values of 28–30/queen/year. Kemper and Döhring (1961) for two of the same species give 16–25.

Hence a value of some 0·07/queen/day is considerably smaller than the productivity of *Bombus*. The more advanced *Paravespula* group which follow the same system of reproduction, and do not protect their young queens, are more productive. Thus *P. germanica* give 168 (Richards and Richards, 1951) or 384/queen/lifetime (an average of several sets of data calculated by Kemper and Döhring, 1961) and *P. vulgaris* with smaller colonies give 107. Hence the former species may reach an *H* of 1/queen/ day and so have a good chance of quickly colonizing any available sites.

The South American Polybiinae were assumed to produce new colonies with the same queen/worker ratio as those ready to swarm (which were easier to find and collect). Values for *G* were then obtained of from 1–4, giving for a lifetime of 9 weeks, an *H* of some 0·06/queen/ day, a value comparable with *Dolichovespula*. However, the Polybiinae reproduce by swarming and the survival of their young queens is probably much higher. The same applies to *Apis mellifera*, which may produce only 20 young queens in a queen's lifetime of about 4 years, giving an *H* of 0·014/queen/day, extremely low.

I know of no data for the sexual production of an ant colony throughout its life, but some estimates of annual production exist. Thus 718 young queens are produced by a large colony of *Myrmica ruginodis macrogyna* which may have some 5 queens (Brian and Brian, 1951). In calculating the productivity it is necessary to include the period of immaturity, say 7 years (Brian, 1957a), so that in a total life of 15 years 8 seasons of 150 queens per queen are produced, making *H* 0·22/queen/ day. This, though probably an underestimate, is quite a large value, comparable with temperate *Bombus* and between *Dolichovespula* and *Paravespula*. In ants the estimation of productivity is complicated by the fact that many nests are immature and produce no sexuals at all, and others produce either one or other sex but not both. Thus *Formica rufa* in a sample of 213 nests gave 18 % with males only, 55 % with females only, and 27 % with both (Gösswald, 1957). Some 2×10^3 were produced per nest on the average in the ratio 5 female to 2 male. Very high sexual production, $8–10 \times 10^3$ per nest, is recorded of *Dolichoderus mariae* Forel by Kannowski (1959b); and $12–15 \times 10^3$ for *D. taschenbergi* Mayr. by Talbot (1956); on the other hand, *Lasius flavus* gave a maximum of 410 queens from one nest in one year (Pontin, 1961b, 1963). In terms of area, it has been recorded of *Pogonomyrmex* in a lucerne (*Medicago sativa* L) field that $2·2 \times 10^5$/ha were emitted, yet no more nests were found next year (Wildermuth and Davis quoted Scherba, 1963).

At the other extreme are the ants that protect and guide their new queens to a selected site, and which produce very few and then usually only in response to a shortage. Raignier (1959) gives 56 as a maximum in one division of a colony of *Dorylus* (*Anomma*) *wilverthi*, and after the division when the young queens hatch all but one are killed. The selected one is not necessarily the oldest, but is perhaps the most attractive, and no doubt this quality must correlate closely with utility to the species if it is to survive. *Eciton*, as is well known, is similar (Schneirla, 1957).

B. SURVIVAL

The shape of the survival curve is unknown, but as most mortality occurs before nests are even started, and since as they grow this probably decreases, not so much because they become less conspicuous (indeed, the reverse is true), but because of their stronger defences, it can be guessed to be negative exponential.

Only 1 in 5 nests started by female *Halictus duplex* reached the matrifilial stage (Sakagami and Hayashida, 1961). Most causes of loss are still unknown. As some 5 females are produced by each nest, the spring number is restored prior to the summer matrifilial stages, and as these co-operate the species population potential is presumably higher. Cumber (1953) records that of 80 *Bombus agrorum* nests 25 died out prematurely (31%), 23 were destroyed by animals or fire, and 32 (40%) survived to produce sexuals. Of the last class only 23 (29%) gave young queens. This seems a high survival to maturity, but the nests were probably not located until quite advanced.

Two Japanese *Polistes* species studied by Yoshikawa (1954) showed that only two out of 69 (3%) produced workers. Such high early mortality is characteristic of European *Vespula* (Scott, 1944; Duncan, 1939). Of 12 nests of *Dolichovespula sylvestris* only 1 matured, 6 died without workers, and 5 produced fewer than 10 workers (Brian and Brian, 1948, 1952). Nests usurped by other queens of the same species were no more successful. Most seemed to fail on account of some weakness of the queen, perhaps actual exhaustion, perhaps disease which caused them to fly badly in the evening and have difficulty in settling into their nest.

In all the above cases no queen lives longer than a year; very few observations on longevity exist where queens live longer than one year, as they are difficult to obtain under natural conditions. The queen *Halictus marginatus* lives 5 or 6 years (Plateau-Quénu, 1962). There is a record of a marked queen of *Melipona quadrifasciata* Lepeletier living 3 years and 1 month after mating (Kerr, Zucchi, Nakadaira and Butolo, 1962). Queen *Apis mellifera* may be lost from observation when they swarm, but Jean-Prost (1956) gives 6 years maximum and found that 75 lived 1 year, 64 lived 2 years, and 50 lived 3 years; 3 or 4 years is regarded as the usual life span. Bozina (1961) says that in normal colonies queen survival is: for 2–3 years, 50 %; for 4–6 years, 30–35 %; for more than 6 years, some; and 2 lived 8 and 1 at least 9 years.

In captivity, ant queens have been known to live 10 years or more (Bodenheimer, 1937a). A recent observation on a marked wild queen of *Eciton burchelli* is 5 years and is the oldest known (Rettenmeyer, 1963a). Vanderplank (1960) found that if the queen *Oecophylla longinoda* was removed the colony died out rather than requeen. Only 30 % of normal ones survived 5 years, most being destroyed by other ants. Of 165 colonies in palms 11 (6·6 %) died out in 3 years and 7 (4 %) emigrated; unfortunately some insecticides were applied.

A favourite method of studying ant colony survival is to mark and measure their mounds. Dreyer and Park (1932), Dreyer (1942), and recently Scherba (1958) have pioneered this method using *Formica ulkei* Emery. From 1931 to 1941 the numbers fell, then remained steady, and in the last census the proportion of medium and large colonies was higher, suggesting an ageing population. During the 10-year period the average rate of decrease was 5 % per annum. Mounds that disappeared did so through shading, through human interference, or from unknown causes. Many new ones started and failed to grow and Scherba calculated their birth rate at 9·1 % (1951) and 16 % (1954), but he comments that new nests are difficult to find. Dreyer (1942) gave 20–25 years as the life span of such mounds, but whether this represents the longevity of the queen or whether several queens were involved is uncertain. Recently Talbot (1961) has described a 6-year study of the mounds of this species in Michigan. She noticed that many were formed and then abandoned: of 56 started only 18 survived 2 years, but 13 remained after 6 years, so that the drop in the first few years is some 60–70 %. These mounds did not necessarily die; they may have returned to their parent colony and so perhaps represent trial buds that proved unsuccessful.

Scherba (1961, 1963) has also studied the colony population dynamics of *Formica opaciventris*, a member of the North American *F. excecta* Nyl. group. This reproduces by budding following pleometrosis, new buds being established in disturbed soil or nests of *F. fusca*. Between 1957 and 1959 the proportion of small nests increased and of medium decreased. A mortality of 8–9 % per annum for all mounds varied regionally, and small mounds had as high as 35 % mortality. There seems to have been little sign of immortality for large mounds; destructive forces and shading, if not the exhaustion of local resources, seem to terminate their lives. Only 20–25 % of mature mounds emitted sexuals in one year and rather fewer another year, an indication probably of cycles of sexual production. A birth rate of 5–16 % per annum varied regionally. Data on *Formica excecta* populations summarized by Scherba show reasonable agreement; a turnover of about 9–10% is indicated. Of 18 small mounds of *Lasius flavus* studied by Waloff and Blackith (1962) only 6 lived 8 years. The decline of the other 12 was associated either with interference by *Myrmica scabrinodis*, which is reported to prey on *L. flavus* whilst living in its mounds, or to changes in the habitat.

The various results discussed agree in suggesting that small mounds readily die either through resorption (if buds), through predation, by human interference, or through shading and other changes in the environment. A small proportion of mounds that become large are more persistent, but more data over longer periods will be needed to understand their history.

As termites are able to replace their reigning sexuals even in their primitive families, colonies might be expected to endure for long periods and to die only when some successional change causes deterioration of the habitat or perhaps when they have exhausted the food supply. However, Grassé (1949) has pointed out that although damaged or destroyed queens are replaced ageing ones may not be (as sometimes in *Apis mellifera*), in which case the colony simply dies out. He suggests 10–15 years for Calotermitidae and longer for *Reticulitermes*, which has a notoriously high rate of neotony. Some Termitidae have been estimated to live several decades, but this is uncertain, as nests may be recolonized by others.

CHAPTER 11

STRUCTURAL LIMITATIONS

Structure and food are the essential resources that cause intraspecific competition and limit population. Each is modified by climate and traffic. All social insects need structures to support or contain nests which shelter them from the environment during sensitive stages of the life cycle, and many require places in which to shelter from bad seasons, and special mating structures.

A. NEST SITES AND SHELTERS

Intrinsic limitations to nest size and shape have already been discussed; here the external conditions that limit the size and number of nests in an area are considered. The nature of competition for these is discussed later.

1. *Structure and size*

Many forms demand only a suitable medium in which to excavate a chamber: usually soil or wood. Nevertheless the plastic properties must be important and influence the speed, durability, and size of the final nest. So, too, will the slope of the soil. In England the ant *Formica rufa* is associated with sandy and siliceous soils (Nelmes, 1938). This may be because they are easier to excavate, but it could be because they drain better and are warmer, for Satchell and Collingwood (1955) found that in the English Lake District this ant is more common on calcareous soil, because this generated an open forest that was comparatively warm and dry. By contrast *Lasius flavus*, whose nest has a much greater mineral content, is associated with calcareous and clay-rich soils in England, probably because of the adhesive properties of clay crumbs. Hard soils are necessary for *Anoplolepis* to nest in South Africa (Steyn, 1958). By contrast, the bee *Halictus duplex* was not found to show much predisposition to any soil type, though the range of variation was comparatively slight (Sakagami and Hayashida, 1961). Waterlogged soil is not a good building medium and most bog ants build with vegetable debris; *Lasius flavus*, a mineral builder, does not make mounds over high water tables (Waloff and Blackith, 1962). Horizontal space under stones may be limiting, for large stones if flat and thick attract *Formica lemani* in

Scotland and *F. fusca* in England, but smaller ones are left to species of *Myrmica*. *Lasius flavus* only uses stones temporarily, building soil over them as their mound grows. On the floor of New Guinea tropical rain forest twigs used as nests by many ants seemed to be limiting in size and number (Wilson, 1959a), and it was suggested that colony size might have evolved to exploit this feature.

Many social insects demand only a support like a leaf or branch from which to hang their nest (e.g. polybiine wasps, Richards and Richards, 1951). The ant *Oecophylla* binds leaves together with larval saliva. The height above ground of a branch may be important: *Eciton hamatum* needs to be able to hang worker-curtains to the ground (Schneirla *et al.*, 1954; Jackson, 1957), and *Apis dorsata* nests higher in trees than *A. florea*, presumably from choice (Butler, 1954a). Clearly where several twigs are involved they must be mechanically related, otherwise they will move differentially in wind.

Nesting in natural holes or holes made by other animals from hollow stems to hollow trees is also common in all groups. If not large enough these must be expandable, and it is interesting that *Apis cerana* Fabr. from the East is better at enlarging its holes than *A. mellifera* (Sakagami, 1959). It is well known that *Bombus* has species that differ in whether they use a hole with a tunnel or a surface depression: both demand vegetable nest material as well.

Perhaps social parasites or ants in myrmecophytic plants show the greatest specificity of nest site.

2. *Climate and microclimate*

Climate influences the number and usefulness of nest sites in two principal ways: by varying the structural complexity through the flora and by varying the microclimate in a given structure.

Tropical rain forest is extremely rich in this way (see Bequaert in Wheeler, 1922b). Wilson (1959a) pointed out how ants nest from the forest floor to the tree crowns, arboreal types being particularly well developed as compared with temperate and boreal forests. They nest in leaves, branches dead or alive, epiphytes, and suspended carton nests, yet most live on the ground in the soil or in twigs. The microclimate is important, thus *Eciton hamatum* when it is in a statary phase, or in the dry season, selects sites in logs and holes that are cooler and moister than its normal sites. As this species is homoiothermic, minimum variation is desirable (Schneirla *et al.*, 1954; Jackson, 1957). Poikilothermic ants may seek insolated spots; like *Anoplolepis custodiens* F. Smith, which only nests under bare soil and by sinking chambers to over a metre can keep its brood day and night at 30°C with only slight vertical movement; under shaded soil 25–26°C is normal (Way, 1953).

Planting species of *Lippia* in citrus orchards reduced this species (Steyn, 1958). The leaf-nesting *Oecophylla* moves its nests seasonally from one side to another of its trees; Vanderplank (1960) has pointed out that this migration is associated with the sun's position and confers full insolation, and Way (1954a) that the nests are sheltered from the prevailing wind.

In desert-nesting ants, soil depth and moisture are important. *Myrmecocystus melliger* Forel may go down 5 m (Creighton and Crandall, 1954) and *Veromessor pergandei* 3–4 m (Tevis, 1958). Yet the most common Saharan ant *Monomorium salomonis* L. has quite superficial nests (Bernard, 1961). Even in west Scotland shallow soils may dry out so that only species making well-mudded nests survive (*Myrmica scabrinodis* in Brian, 1956d).

In boreal regions insolation increases in importance, and may be essential even for homoiothermic species, e.g. *Formica rufa* (Raignier, 1948). In both the Alps (Ronchetti, 1963) and the British Isles (Yarrow, 1955) this species inhabits warmer areas than related ones. Quite short herbs can give lethal shade: thus bracken (*Pteridium acquilinum* L.) grows up after tree cutting and is probably responsible for the reduced range of *F. rufa* in the English Lake District (Satchell and Collingwood, 1955). *Lasius flavus*, which can build large strong mounds in lightly grazed grassland, has been shaded out by *Calluna vulgaris* L., or the tall grass *Arrhenatherum elatior* L. (Waloff and Blackith, 1962) or by a coarse inedible grass *Brachypodium pinnatum* L. (Pontin, 1963). In these cases food may have become poorer as well, for Aphidae are cultured on the grass roots.

The majority of ants depend on grazing herbivores to keep down the vegetation near their nests, but a few species are able to prevent vegetation growing themselves. A good example is *Pogonomyrmex barbatus*, which in a mixed prickly pear and short grass vegetation denudes roughly circular areas of some 1·4m². Round these areas seeds grow, especially of the grass *Aristida oligantha* (Box, 1960).

The influence of insolation quota on the ant *Myrmica* has been studied by Brian and Brian (1951) and Brian (1956b). In grassland under stones, insulated by air from the soil, these ants showed more brood progress than in the small mounds that they build themselves. The genus does not occur in closed canopy woodland, but does occur in glades as small colonies with small workers and no ability to produce sexuals. Colony and worker size correlated positively with the possible hours of sunshine in a set of glades of different sizes and the partial correlations and path analysis (Brian, 1956b) indicated that insolation probably influenced worker and colony sizes independently (young colonies of less than 300 workers which, as already mentioned, do show regression of worker size on colony size were not present in the sample). It was found by placing cultures in these glades with ample food that normal-sized individuals resulted, though development was considerably slower, and that there was much greater mortality in the transition from larval to adult stages, an effect which would, of course, produce small colonies. The low soil temperatures therefore caused small colony size, not small worker size; and in general it may be said that cool nest sites give small colonies and cooler ones none at all. Unfortunately the relation between size of colony, glade size, and the density of colonies and individuals was not ascertained.

Mature virgin forest in the Alps was cooler and moister than plantation (Adeli, 1962). It held fewer species of ants, and only one-quarter the number of nests and these were also smaller. Food was also sparser, but experimental analysis was not attempted.

For a given glade pattern, the warmer and sunnier the climate the more glades will be inhabitable and the more larger nests they will contain. In fact, *Myrmica ruginodis*, which only occurs in the open in Scotland, occurs in much shadier woodland in southern England and on the Continent. Hours of sunlight are probably more important than air temperature, for they can raise a nest microclimate above equatorial air temperature without loss of humidity. The coastal area of southern and western England and Wales has a higher sunlight average than inland, a fact which may well account for the well-known coastal distribution of certain otherwise continental ants (*Tetramorium caespitum*, *Tapinoma erraticum* Latr.). The limit of the latter species' distribution is closely paralleled by the 7 hours June sunshine limit. Another continental species, *Lasius alienus* Foerst, fits the $6\frac{1}{2}$-hour line quite well (Brian, 1964b).

The early stages of colony foundation are probably more dependent on sun-warmed soil than the later ones, which can to some extent improve their own situation. Probably queen ants descend in rising air or detect heat radiation from hot earth. Queens of *Myrmica ruginodis* and *Formica lemani* settled in freshly cleared woodland rather than grassland near by (Brian, 1952b). On old rotting tree stumps they tended to aggregate on the south side and sought temperatures of 25–30°C in captivity. Soil distributed by animals is often attractive (Scherba, 1963). Waloff (1957) used this to trap *Lasius* queens, and Pontin (1960a) has found that *Lasius* queens settle in bare soil rather than nearby vegetated areas.

This section has been illustrated by reference to ants which comprise a great variety of poikilothermic types. The wasp *Polistes chinensis*, which chooses sunlit places to start nests in and succeeds better in them, has been mentioned. The bee *Halictus duplex*, like most of its family, chooses insolated places in which to excavate a burrow (Sakagami and Haya-shida, 1961). In temperate regions bees and wasps are largely homoio-thermic and seek insulated rather than insolated sites. Thus *Bombus* choose shaded places often underground for nesting, and hibernate in north-facing banks (Free and Butler, 1959). Lindauer (1955a, 1961), who offered swarms of *Apis mellifera* a choice of sites and tapped the ensuing conversation, found that they preferred waterproof, draughtless cavities, and seemed to prefer heat-insulated ones, too; but the most important factor was a need for shelter from wind, which was assessed over a period of several days. This is very important in winter, for small colonies often die out in damp, cold hives; Schuà (1955) found that they succumbed to a fungus disease after warm fronts had passed, and to the sporozoon *Nosema* in cold periods, especially towards spring. Shelter from wind and rain is no doubt important in tree-nesting forms. Rain-fall can erode nests very seriously: Harris (1956) has attributed the variation in the shape of *Macrotermes bellicosus* Smeath mounds to the variation in rainfall intensity as well as soil type. Other termites have gutters on their nests to shed water. In the English Lake District rain can wash the material of *Formica* nests away as quickly as it is gathered (Satchell and Collingwood, 1955). Flooding frequently destroys nests of *Bombus* in Sweden (Bingefors et al., 1960; Fridén, 1960, 1961; Eskilsson and Fridén, 1962), but ants can survive waterlogged conditions if temperature is low and respiratory rate slight by enclosing air spaces in their clusters. Williams (1959b) mentions that many colonies of *Cubitermes ugandensis* (Termitidae) are destroyed by flooding.

3. *Traffic and hazards*

The movements of large animals may cause a lot of damage to the other occupants of an ecosystem in a density-independent way. Their effect on nest sites can be avoided by nesting under a bush, away from paths, underground, in holes in trees and so on. Small mammals can also be a nuisance, as Gösswald and Kloft (1961) have shown; various species of field mice damaged the domes of *Formica rufa* nests whilst searching for seeds and *Cetonia* larvae. "Anting" by birds may be classified here, too. Today the main disturbance is due to man and his domestic animals. Trampling and cultivation destroys many ant and bee nests and severely restricts the areas that are inhabitable. Nest-making pairs of the soil-eating termite *Cubitermes ugandensis* (Termitidae) are often destroyed by trampling (Williams, 1959a). Curiously the human factor has led in Sweden to a reduction in the hole-nesting *Bombus* rather than the surface-nesting ones, which have slightly in-creased (loc. cit.). The action here may well be through the rodent population.

B. MATING STRUCTURES

Many social insects require special features for mating. Little is known about how essential a structure is, what its minimum requirements are or how far individuals will fly to seek it, but in an area poorly supplied with these mating success may well be materially reduced. Here only the structures themselves are discussed; the way in which they are used is mentioned under intraspecies competition.

Bees of the genus *Bombus* either have one fixed station or a circuit of stations marked out each morning by mandibular gland secretion. The essential appears to be some vegetational and topographical variation. Thus some species mark on tree-tops, others on bushes, on herbs, or even on the soil surface. There are indications that if the chosen level is not represented in a district others will be used (Free and Butler, 1959). Male Meliponid bees congregate outside nest entrances, forming compact groups (Michener and Michener, 1951). The drones of *Apis mellifera* congregate, but not a lot is known about the type of area chosen, except that they react to queens only at altitudes greater than 7 m, in open but sheltered places, not over water (Gary, 1963; Zimarlicki and Morse, 1963; Ruttner and Ruttner, 1963); over trees or on the tops of hills have been suggested. *Vespula* wasps have been recorded congregating on the tops of hills (Wynne-Edwards, 1962).

Ant mating requirements are very variable. Most European species of *Myrmica* aggregate round objects that stand up from their surroundings such as trees, houses, and summits, and they fly in the shelter of these (Brian and Brian, 1955); but there are also indications that the conjunction of a light-reflecting plane surface (such as a path or roof) on which they alight and copulate is desirable, though perhaps not essential. Such "open spots" were sufficient to focus males of *Pheidole sitarches* Wheeler (Wilson, 1957). Clusters of *Araucomyrmex tener* (Mayr) males in western Argentina did not drift, but flickered in the breeze, and as there were no trees or houses in the mountain valley, if they were orientating, as seems likely, they must have used some ground pattern (Weber, 1963a). Other species (e.g. *Lasius niger*, *L. flavus*) collect in the convection currents over hills and the males may form clusters, but these show little apparent fixation, for they allow themselves to drift freely in lateral air movements, though, of course, as in all massive mating flights anticyclonic weather with minimal air drift is chosen.

Ant flights are by no means always massive: the genus *Formica* has characteristically sparse flights (Kannowski, 1959b), though Marikovsky (1961) has recorded *Formica rufa* assembling in gorges in the forests of Tien-Shan. In other species the males seem to enter the nest or migrating column to fertilize the females, e.g. *Eciton, Oecophylla*

(Vanderplank, 1960) and *Iridomyrmex humilis* Mayr (Skaife, 1954). This behaviour is particularly valuable in pleometrotic forms that generate their own subsidiary queens, for, of course, it enables cross-fertilization. In some social parasites the males are apterous.

Termites are renowned for their massive synchronous flights (Weesner, 1960), though they have subsidiary ones, too. They are much weaker flyers on the whole than ants and do not disperse as far. Nor do they appear to aggregate in clusters like many social Hymenoptera (and of course Diptera), for the only record is that for *Allognathotermes hypogeus* Silv. (Termitidae), which fly in groups on the sheltered sides of tree-tops, pair on the foliage, and then descend together to earth (Noirot and Bodot, 1964).

As with nesting structures, climate influences the character and suitability of mating stations. Wind is the main disturbance in these flights, though, of course, neither humidity nor temperature must depart too much from optimum. Wind is particularly disturbing in those which do not fix visually, but all forms choose anticyclonic weather in temperate regions, and in dry areas flights are usually associated with rainfall. However, where anticyclonic conditions are rare mating may be impracticable for long periods and in windy places only species that can aggregate in sheltered spots may be able to exist. In the British Isles many queen *Apis mellifera* fail to mate at the appropriate stage of maturity and the whole colony dies out.

CHAPTER 12

FOOD SUPPLY

Food supply may limit population and affect its density and organization. As a prelude to considering competition for food in the next section, feeding methods and factors that modify the availability of food are briefly surveyed, but a general review of the subject is beyond the scope of this book.

A. TYPES OF FOOD

As is usual in animals, successful social insects tend to be either highly specialized or very generalized in their feeding relationships. The specialists have usually established a mutualistic relationship such as bees and flowers, ants and bugs, termites or ants and fungi, whereas the non-specialists have acquired the ability to recognize food (protein and carbohydrate at least) through a variety of disguises, and have particularly associated themselves with man's food stores and waste.

Bees and termites are, of course, largely phytophagous; the former feeding from flowers and plant exudates, the latter on wood, lichens, grass seeds, humus, and a variety of vegetable debris; wasps are mainly predaceous, though they obtain sugars from plants and certain *Paravespula* have generalized their feeding considerably; ants began as predators more or less specialized, and evolved for the most part either towards plant eating (though not abandoning their predatory habits altogether) or towards highly organized polyphagous predation or very specialized predation (such as Dacetini, Wilson, 1953b, 1962d). Thus, the primitive subfamily Ponerinae, which includes many specialist predators, may be found as many small colonies on the rain-forest floor in New Guinea (Wilson, 1959a), whereas most higher subfamilies which culture bugs of some sort have larger colonies, and the legionary Dorylinae, the largest of all.

Plant eating undoubtedly saves energy in locomotion, though it may not be a rich food. Plant seeds are commonly collected by ants in dry climates, but do not, as might be expected, have a higher calorific content than insects (Golley and Gentry, 1964). Many seeds are fully eaten, others just lose their embryo, and still others have a caruncle which alone is destroyed, a feature that may well introduce a mutualistic relationship, the plant gaining dispersal (Bequaert in Wheeler, 1922b). Many seeds appear to be rejected anyway and they germinate within easy foraging distance of the nest, as they are often covered by excavated soil and rubbish; this, of course, provides a proximate source of food. The seed-collecting habits of *Veromessor pergandei* have recently been described by Tevis (1958). This ant extends into steppe and semi-desert and collects the seeds of ephemerals first from the capsules then from the ground. They show a marked preference for some species (not the commonest) and only take less attractive seeds as the supply dwindles, and it is these that enable them to survive periods when winter rain is insufficient to germinate the plants. Enough seeds always seem to get covered by sand to keep the plants going. Strictly speaking these ants are never short of food, though the colonies are smaller in desert than in areas which have perennating plants.

An extremely common plant food for ants is sap, collected after it has been forced through Homoptera of various sorts and modified in various ways (reviewed Way, 1963). It contains amino-acids, minerals, and sugars, and is theoretically a complete food, though this is difficult to confirm in practice and is still open to doubt. Some of the sugars are converted to melezitose which may be harmful, but ant attendance which increases the flow of honeydew and its amino-acid content also reduces the melezitose concentration.

Apart from their honeydew there is increasing evidence that bugs are used as prey, sometimes only stray or old ones being killed (Ledoux, 1950), but in a few cases systematic culling has been noted. The tropical arboricolous ant *Oecophylla longinoda* was shown by Way (1954b) to cultivate a coccid (*Saissetia*) in this way. Apparently excess honeydew induces aggressiveness in a small percentage of workers (large dark ones), which destroy both young and old coccids until the demand for sugars again rises and so on, cyclically. Small pale workers tend a variety of coccids which are eaten and destroyed by large dark ones (Vanderplank, 1960). Way suggests that soil dwellers have a less intensive relationship and Pontin (1958, 1960b) has shown that myrmecophilous aphids of all ages and types are eaten by *Lasius flavus*. They appear to be treated as brood, and are protected in the nest over winter and moved out to plants in spring.

Certain tribes of ants and termites have evolved fungus cultivation. In ants it appears to have come from a habit of collecting the faecal pellets of other insects and making fungus gardens of them. Advanced cultivators cut and collect plant material, mix it with their own faeces and so set up a short-cycle mineral-reclamation process (Weber, 1956, 1958, 1962, 1963b). In termites a similar mutualism seems to have evolved, though the extent and specificity of the relationship is not yet fully worked out (Sands, 1956, 1960; Weesner, 1960; Grassé and Noirot, 1961).

B. FOOD COLLECTION

A very great deal of work has been done on this subject recently, but there is no comprehensive review for social insects. Here it is only possible to mention the main results cursorily, and only in their relevance to population size.

The simplest system of food collection involves individual activity with little or no mutual influence. This is so in *Bombus*, where workers may establish routines, though it is possible that new foragers are influenced by the type of food the older ones bring in (A. D. Brian, 1954; Free and Butler, 1959). A useful addition to this is the ability to stimulate increased foraging intensity if food is found. *Formica fusca* is of this type (Dobrzanska, 1958, 1959; Wallis, 1963), and it is possible that many *Formica* species are no more highly organized, thus individual workers of *F. rufa* forage quite restricted areas (Otto, 1958b). There is evidence that some ants (Sudd, 1959; Wilson, 1959b) and wasps (Lindauer, 1961) may lead recruited foragers to a food source (piloting), but a very common development of this is to lay a trail. Both occur together in Meliponidae (Lindauer and Kerr, 1960; Lindauer, 1961) and it is curious that *Bombus* has males that lay trails and females that may occasionally pilot, but these have not been combined in one sex. Trails and group retrieving are well developed in many ants which appear to need only a small number of scouts out at any time. The nature of the chemical used is very important here: it must be persistent, but not too persistent. The trail of *Solenopsis saevissima* F. Smith evaporates on glass in still air in 104 seconds and its maximum length, depending on the rate of movement of the ant, is 42 cm (Wilson, 1958a, 1962b, c, d; Wilson and Bossert, 1963; Sudd, 1957, 1960).

Bees of the genus *Apis* communicate distance as well as direction (though only in two dimensions) analogistically and they also have strong localization tendencies in individual foraging (Esch, 1956; Lindauer, 1961; Wenner, 1964). Different subspecies vary in their ability to communicate direction near the hive, and the small species *A. florea* uses a larger-scale representation than *A. mellifera*, thus mapping a smaller area more precisely. *Apis mellifera* alone symbolizes solar direction in terms of gravity.

Finally there is group raiding (Wilson, 1958a) that is highly developed in some ants of the genus *Leptogenys* (Ponerinae) and all Dorylinae. This is accompanied by frequent changes of locus, so that the colonies virtually wander over large areas in search of food, though, as Schneirla (1949) stresses, not because they have exhausted an area, rather in response to an internal brood change. Its behavioural basis has been fully analysed by Schneirla (summarized 1957), Rettenmeyer (1963a),

and Raignier and van Boven (1955). As a hunting method it is analog-
ous to mammalian foraging and is, of course, quite inappropriate to
agriculture. The ground raids of *Oecophylla longinoda* from fixed bases are
similar (Ledoux, 1950), as also is slave raiding by *Formica sanguinea* and
Polyergus rufescens Latr. (Dobrzanski, 1961; Dobrzanska and Dobrzanski, 1960, 1962), though Wilson (1958a) prefers to classify this
otherwise.

Sedentary species often support these various foraging techniques by
a permanent system of trackways above or below ground (Chauvin,
1962; Sudd, 1958). This is especially well developed in termites, for
even tree nesters make covered tracks to the ground (Weesner, 1960).
The workers of *Hospitalitermes* forage at night for lichens and algae on
tree trunks which they roll into pellets, different workers apparently
carrying them back to the nest (Kalshoven, 1958); such a division of
labour may be more common than is suspected (Weesner, 1960).

C. MODIFYING FACTORS

1. *Climatic influence*

Climate influences food supply both directly and, by interfering with
food collection, indirectly. Where it is very variable scouting and recruitment or covered permanent ways clearly help to minimize exposure.

In temperate regions it is important that a species does not come out
of hibernation too soon, for food may be inadequate. Thus *Lasioglossum
zephyrum* has subnormal amounts of pollen in its cells in spring (Batra,
1964). *Bombus* species may be unable to collect enough in a day to last
the night and their temperature falls (A. D. Brian, 1954), and Cumber
(1953) thought that pollen which is mainly available on *Salix* bushes
limited population growth. *Apis mellifera* in east Scotland showed a
positive partial correlation between pollen store and brood number
(colony size fixed) during the months October to March, especially in
December and January. This is the time of the year when these bees
are resuming growth and are entirely dependent on stored pollen for
this. Even when flowers are available the rate of use of pollen may
exceed its supply and stores continue to be used up (Allen and Jeffree,
1956, 1957).

Drought in summer is also responsible for lack of food. As much as
1·2 kg of pollen may be stored by a moderate-sized colony of *Apis
mellifera* (4×10^4 bees) in summer, but there is only a significant partial
correlation between this and brood number in July, which is a month
when forage is not only reduced but especially liable to water shortage
(Allen and Jeffree, 1956, 1957). Rashad and Parker (1958), using a
pollen trap through the season, found that pollen was limiting in dry

years in summer. It is a common observation that honey-bees seek honeydew on deep-rooting forest trees at times when herbs have dried up and many newly formed colonies die.

Foraging in summer is affected by weather. A genus notably resistant to wind, rain, and cold as well as low light intensity is *Bombus*. In the tropics, however, it either forages morning and evening or lives only in mountains (A. D. Brian, 1954). Many ants show this diurnal variation, a recent example being that of *Veromessor pergandei* in desert (Tevis, 1958).

The restricting effect of climate in woodland in Scotland on the ant *Myrmica ruginodis* has already been mentioned. Shortage of sunlight reduces the herb flora and hence the food supply near the nest (which is on the soil surface), and the workers have to climb trees for food. This leads to small individuals and an inability to produce sexuals. Colonies are also small.

2. *Traffic and other hazards*

The possible damage which animal movement causes to food supply needs no emphasis. For those ants that depend on grasses the role of ungulates is interesting: by their trampling and feeding they destroy many of the herbs and tree seedlings, and they maim insects enough to make them easily caught. But they may also damage the nest mounds, though there are indications that heavy domestic cattle do not tread on mounds of *Lasius flavus* even though they feed off them. Other lighter grazers like rabbits (*Oryctolagus cuniculus* L.) both feed off them, trample on them lightly (without damage) and above all defaecate on them— this apparently because they like resting on elevated structures which give them all-round visibility. This mutualistic relation between ants and rabbits has been considered by Elton (1927).

Fire must often be disastrous locally to tree- and surface-nesting insects. Near Tomsk large numbers of *Formica rufa* group ants are destroyed by fire, which leads to a reversion to a solitary form, but whether by regression of one stock or infiltration of new colonies perhaps of a different species is not clear (Marikovsky, 1962b). To those that live beneath the soil or in non-combustible mounds (ants and termites) it is less damaging and may be an essential ingredient of their biome, preventing tree growth.

CHAPTER 13

INTRASPECIFIC COMPETITION

Milne's definition of competition in relation to a unit of resource (Milne, 1961) means that during the dispersion of a species over a resource competition is likely to occur more often the greater the ratio of population to resource. When a resource is uniformly distributed, or nearly so, an overdispersed pattern (index of dispersion less than unity) will indicate intense competition. Park's distinction between exploitation and interference, which separates competition that does not involve any attempt to oust established individuals from that which does, is useful (Park, 1954) and is implicit in theoretical models (Brian, 1956c). Success in exploitation goes to those species that are skilful detectors of resources and that act rapidly and decisively; success in interference goes to those that have well-developed offensive methods. All need some form of defensive procedure.

A. MODE OF DISPERSION

Ants and termites provide examples of overdispersion. Talbot (1943, 1954) suggested that the nests of *Prenolepis imparis* Say and of *Aphaenogaster treatae* were overdispersed. This was confirmed by Brian (1956b). Colonies of *Myrmica ruginodis macrogyna* showed tendencies to overdispersion in acid grassland, and old tree stumps had 1, rarely 2, nests on them, again significant overdispersion (Brian, 1956b). A similar relationship in sticks on the New Guinea rain-forest floor has been mentioned (Wilson, 1959a). *Lasius flavus* is overdispersed in dense communities, but randomly dispersed in sparse ones, and in the former case an equilateral triangular pattern was approached (Waloff and Blackith, 1962). *Formica fusca* in grassland on Mount Hakkôda (Japan) was overdispersed in a central, fairly uniform region where it was almost pure but of curiously low density, whereas in a higher-density, species-rich area marginal to woodland it was aggregated (Yasuno, 1964). The main other species was *F. truncorum* Forel. Similar distributions are well known for termites; thus the mound nests of *Coptotermes brunneus* Gay in semi-arid western Australia when dense are spaced about 90 m apart and have no young colonies between them, and the tree-nesting *C. acinaformis* Froggatt in the forests of eastern Australia shows a similar pattern (Greaves, 1962).

On the other hand, bees and wasps do not show these overdispersed distributions. It is well known that halictine bees aggregate; thus *Halictus duplex* nests in soil that has morning sunshine, in clusters with an index of dispersion of 1·9 and a frequency distribution that fits the Polya-Eggenberger series (Sakagami and Hayashida, 1961). Nests in densely occupied areas were more successful than outliers, perhaps through improved defence against Mutillids (Michener, 1958; Lin, 1964), and in the circumstances there is every reason why a tendency to return to the same site should be selected even though equally good sites are vacant. A good example from wasps is that of *Polybia rejecta* Fabricius, which nests in trees occupied by dolichoderine ants in the South American tropics and of which Richards and Richards (1951) record one tree with at least 8 nests of varying sizes, as well as other aculeate Hymenoptera. *Bombus* nests of a single species occur in favourable sites—21 B. agrorum nests in a 0·8 ha rubbish heap were discovered by Cumber (1953) along with other species of this genus. There is nothing to indicate whether or not such favourable nesting zones are saturated, as the structural feature is probably not evenly dispersed itself. Only in the case of *Halictus* is there evidence of non-random distribution within the favourable area.

The difference between these two modes of distribution, dispersed nests in a feeding area and the grouped nests outside, the solitary and the colonial habit (in terms of colonies) respectively is presumably to do with the fact that bees and wasps can all fly, whereas ants and termites cannot. This gives the former a larger, sparser foraging area and probably enables them to be more exacting about nest-site structure.

B. METHODS OF DISPERSION

This is a complicated process, whose basic behavioural mechanisms are hardly known in social insects (see Ribbands, 1964). Competition is necessary if intraspecific selection is to be effective, but there seems to be no good reason why actual combat should be involved, and it would be expected that orderly methods of selection (contest) and distribution might have been evolved in social Hymenoptera, as they have so outstandingly been in parasitoid members of the order (Salt, 1961).

1. *Territory*

(a) *Individual*. Primitive bees and wasps show vestigial individual territories in nests (Michener and Wille, 1961; Batra, 1964). In *Lasioglossum zephyrum* (Halictinae) in spring, when pollen is difficult to get, too many cells are made and each is inadequately provisioned and females destroy each others' eggs and substitute their own. In *Bombus* and *Polistes* the females compete for cells in which to lay, eat each others' eggs and establish dominance systems that influence the places that they can stand or rest in and the type of activity they can manifest (reviewed Brian, 1964a).

Outside the nests, individual foraging areas do occur even in advanced forms. Thus *Bombus* workers tend to have routine foraging circuits and to frequent restricted areas, though this does not prevent their collecting mixed pollen loads (A. D. Brian, 1954; Free and Butler, 1959; Miyamoto, 1960). Even *Apis mellifera* has a well-defined locality fixation which may involve individual hostility, as Weaver (1957) found on *Vicia villosa*, where bees threatened or provoked actual collision, especially if nectar was scarce, when they wandered about more, though if it was abundant they might reach $4/m^2$ without hostility. Hunger increases the aggressiveness of *Formica fusca* (Wallis, 1962a). It is common observation that bees and wasps may reach densities on favoured plants, like *Cotoneaster*, that cause so much interference that little collecting is possible.

Ants of the genus *Formica* are reported to have individual foraging areas, though they are not hostile to others (Dobrzanska, 1958; Otto, 1958a).

(*b*) *Nest*. All social insects protect their nests from a wide variety of other animals. Entrances are few, small, and guarded. Whilst recognition of different species and genera is easy, this is not so for members of the same species; and although progress has recently been made with this problem much remains to be done (see Free and Butler, 1959; Wilson, 1963b; Ribbands, 1964). Different species appear to rely in different degrees on mixtures of endogenous and adventitious chemicals. Ledoux (1950) demonstrated how the polycalic *Oecophylla longinoda* can diverge so that the parts on remeeting show hostility. A few months' separation suffices. Presumably the identity of a colony depends on continuous mixing of individuals as well as interchange of food. A similar situation exists in *Formica polyctena* (Marikovsky, 1962b).

Most competition for nest sites occurs between the queen foundresses. *Allodapula* females may often be found in hollow stems that are obviously unsuitable and usually too small (Michener, 1962). There are numerous records of queens of *Bombus* and *Vespula* found dead in the entrances to nests of the same species, and there is no doubt that competition is frequent (Sladen, 1912; Richards, 1953; Free and Butler, 1959; Brian and Brian, 1951).

Interactions between mature colonies that result in nests changing occupancy are frequently recorded in ants, though more often between than within species. The attackers invariably behave extranidally and in a way that makes it difficult to decide whether food or nest sites are, in fact, under competition. This is discussed later in this section. However, a relevant case in Meliponid bees in which a strong colony of

Plebeia (Friesella) schrottkyi Friese exterminates a small colony and occupies its nest is described by Moure *et al.* (1958).

(c) *Food.* As bees and wasps fly and forage extensively, the establishment of a territory would be difficult. However, individual defended zones and a tendency to disperse no farther than necessary would certainly create a territory without the necessity to recognize alien bees in the field. Thus *Apis mellifera* colonies whose feeding organization on *Vicia villosa* has just been mentioned have been shown to interfere with each others' dispersal by tagging with radioisotope (Levin, 1961). On *Medicago sativa* the foraging area of a hive was reduced by surrounding it with others (Levin and Glowska-Konopacka, 1963). On sugar dishes bees from different colonies of the same subspecies can distinguish each other, for they fight as the dish dries up, but are unable to monopolize it (Kalmus, 1941) unless they are of different subspecies, in which case they are noticeably more hostile.

Ant territory has been widely studied since Elton (1932) showed its existence in *Formica rufa*. It probably evolved as an extension from the nest, which is fiercely guarded (Chauvin, 1962), to groups of Homoptera around which shelters were probably built. In *Myrmica ruginodis* and probably other ants recognition of an individual of a different colony of the same species involves close examination and this makes grappling inevitable, but recognition of different species is possible at a greater distance (a centimetre or so) and contact can be avoided (Brian, 1955). This enables small durable food sources to be protected from the same species only if they are discovered early and well populated with workers; intruders from different colonies will thus be grasped and carried back to the nest, a perfectly manageable state of affairs as long as they do not come in too great a number at any time. Another example is the monopolization of fallen fruit by *Prenolepis imparis*, which lasts as long as the fruit remains (Talbot, 1943).

Traffic naturally occurs between food sources and the nest and scouts and hunters tend to spread out from these areas. Though they do not monopolize or defend them in any way, they establish for themselves a high probability of finding and acquiring any food particles that arise in such zones. In this way even the foraging areas of isolated nests of *Myrmica* may be highly asymmetric and when there are several colonies together they tend to fit into a mosaic (Brian, 1955).

A more effective exclusion of other colonies is attained if permanent foraging trackways above or below ground are established, as they can be if food sources are permanent, for these tracks cannot intersect without fighting, which, of course, leads to avoidance, and this, except in structurely very complex habitats, necessitates spatial separation. These route networks can be regarded as extensions of the nest structure.

Formica rufa is an example: trees and aphids are rarely shared, and if they are, then the ants from different colonies pass on appropriate sides of the trunks and use different branches (Elton, 1932; Raignier, 1952; Holt, 1955). *F. sanguinea* has a similar system of trackways to nests and its slave *F. fusca* (Talbot and Kennedy, 1940). In the Alps *F. polyctena* has larger territories in virgin forest than in plantation (Adeli, 1962), and this is attributed to relative scarcity of food in the former. Routes to bugs are longer but fewer. Speaking of this species and of *F. rufa*, Marikovsky (1956, 1962b) says that combats between colonies are particularly frequent in overpopulated areas obviously short of food, and that this is the principal method of control.

An ant renowned for its hostility to most other insects is the leaf-nesting tropical *Oecophylla longinoda*. Several trees are occupied by one colony, connected by ground tracks, and as the leaves of trees are used as nests after being spun together it can be supposed that the whole group of trees is regarded as a nest and so defended. In addition various coccids are cultured on the trees in a closely mutualistic predator-prey relationship as already described. Moreover, the alien insects caught on the tree provide a valuable source of food as well. So the whole set of trees can be regarded as a combined nesting and feeding zone (Ledoux, 1950; Way, 1954a and b; Vanderplank, 1960). Apart from the tracks connecting trees, these ants occasionally hunt on the soil near the base of the trees, though this is not fiercely defended. They also send out organized raids that proceed rectilinearly and have a protective skin of stationary major workers. These raids may last a day and both prey and honeydew are collected (Ledoux, 1950). An interesting feature is that they only come from large colonies (with over 15 nests) and they sometimes establish a bud in one of the raided trees. Perhaps this depends on the quality of food found and the degree of opposition.

On the intraspecific level now being considered the main function of territory is to prevent new colonies starting up in the zones where established ones need to feed. Again there are numerous examples in ants (e.g. Marikovsky, 1962b), but it is interesting that even *Apis mellifera* workers are reported to attack flying queens of their own species, especially near their hive (Ruttner and Ruttner, 1963). Pontin (1960a) has experimented with queens of *Lasius niger* and *Lasius flavus* by settling them in tubes that were only worker permeable and putting them in the territory of established colonies. He was able to provide evidence that intraspecific reaction was fiercer than interspecific reaction, and like queens were sooner destroyed than unlike ones.

There are also many records in the older literature (e.g. Forel, 1928) of large colonies destroying smaller ones. Often this involves a siege that ends with the sudden evacuation of the besieged colony and a later occupation by the besieger (e.g. *Myrmica scabrinodis* described by Brian, 1952a). Again a direct attack chamber by chamber with the invader grabbing, poisoning, dragging out, and dismembering or taking back to the nest the invaded individuals one at a time is a frequent process. Both in offence and defence soil barriers may be used as shields and lengthy salients established by pushing forward in cracks and crevices or underground galleries, a method which can sometimes effectively cut communications. Massing in strategic places as at the base of tree trunks or outside nests is also a common feature. During these assimilations the brood is not necessarily destroyed and may be incorporated in the larger colony, but whether or not this happens is likely to depend on the degree of genetic resemblance between the colonies.

There is no doubt that many termite colonies destroy queens that settle in their foraging area. Greaves (1960, 1962) has noted this of *Coptotermes brunneus*; also that in areas where competition for trees is intense one colony may take over galleries of another of the same species. A very interesting fusion of young colonies has been recorded by Kalshoven (1959) of *Neotermes tectonae*, a species that lives in dead teak branches. He found that laboratory cultures often fused and destroyed only one of the royal pairs, but he thinks that in nature they may grow bigger before fusing. Such peaceful assimilation with regulation of the reproductive number is clearly more efficient than the commonly observed massacre that occurs in similar circumstances among ants.

The method of dispersion of army ants (Dorylinae) should be interesting when it is fully explored. The raiding zones of different colonies of *Eciton hamatum* seldom overlap, even partially on successive days (Schneirla, 1949). Rettenmeyer (1963a) says of this species that if raiding columns of different colonies meet some inconclusive fighting occurs and a skin is then formed of orientated workers which only attack individuals which transgress the line. Often a plant bridge enables them to avoid each other, or else they move away. It would be interesting to know if this behaviour changes when through higher densities contacts become more frequent. The maintenance of individuality in these cases is evidently helped by the queen, for queenless columns fuse with others though the brood and many workers are killed. Raignier and van Boven (1955) record absence of hostility between colonies of *Dorylus* (*Anomma*) species, though as they are known to be organized on a colony basis it would appear that at least they avoid mixing.

2. *Aggregation and pleometrosis*

In some social insects, as in some vertebrates, peaceful methods of dispersion have evolved. Paradoxically these often involve aggregation as a first step, followed by organization. In this way species material is conserved and held in reserve, only its disruptive antisocial behaviour being stopped.

An excellent example of this in a fairly primitive wasp, *Polistes*, is now well known. Queens wishing to found nests are not destroyed if they enter one already started by another; they are incorporated and dominated so that they function as virtually sterile assistants. But if the queen dies or fails they are able to replace her. Co-operative groups of ants have also been discussed in an earlier section. The only peculiar feature was the dispersion of *Lasius flavus*, once the pupal stage had been reached, into small groups that must surely have met again after some growth.

Secondary pleometrosis may be facultative. The queens of *Camponotus ligniperda* Latr. are able to start colonies by themselves, but are intensely hostile to each other and rarely co-operate. If they start new nest, within range of an established one, they are collected by the workerss who find them more attractive than their own virgins and take them in; but they continue to avoid each other (Hölldobler, 1962). Queens of *Myrmica rubra* can just found colonies alone, though they do better in groups, and are also accepted into colonies or allowed to stay and be fertilized in their own colony. This is probably a cyclic process being generated by a relative shortage of queens and stopped by their recruitment. The tropical *Anoplolepis longipes* Jerb. is probably of this type, for Way (1953) has said that it occurs as isolated colonies and as pleometrotic aggregates, the latter at high densities; so also *Formica rufa*, according to Marikovsky (1962b).

Obligatorily pleometrotic species reconnoitre from their parent nest. Groups of workers collect in desirable subsidiary sites and sooner or later take brood and queens, or collect them after nuptials as already described. It is likely that the worker parties assess the food supply as well as the nest site, but there is not a lot of evidence for this. Ledoux (1950) in describing raids of *Oecophylla* pointed out that they sometimes resulted in new colonies. There is a distinct similarity here with the Dorylinae: *Eciton* emigrates only after a major raid, moving along trails that are returning more booty and establishing a new bivouac in that direction, often at a junction, provided the microclimate is suitable (Schneirla, 1949). *Apis mellifera* swarms do not enter a nest site unless they can fill their crops in the locality (Martin, 1963), and it is known that *Apis dorsata* and *A. florea* are much more sensitive to local food conditions and migrate regularly, whereas *A. mellifera* only occasionally does so. It is possible that competition intensity is also assessed in a new habitat, and there may also be an innate tendency to move a certain distance, as Lindauer (1955a, 1961) found that they preferred to settle some distance away from the parent colony, even though difficulties arose over moving the queen.

Whereas the evolution of pleometrosis and reproduction by fission has proceeded without any obvious drawbacks in bees and wasps, ants and termites, whose workers are apterous, have inevitably lost dispersal power unless they have retained the ability to reproduce by single queens (or pairs) as well. It is readily appreciated that in a stable favourable habitat some degeneration of queen independence could occur, for the selective pressure to maintain large amply provided queens must be considerable. The analogy with *Malacosma pluviae* (Dyar), in which as a population ages the proportion of larvae that are dependent on web societies for survival increases (Wellington, 1960), is worth mentioning. However, this has happened, as both ants and termites have wholly pleometrotic species and they are often successful ones, though much of this may be due to their ability to move small buds by human transport (e.g. *Iridomyrmex humilis, Monomorium pharaonis*, and others). Others have been less successful and are now relict patchy populations, as Wilson (1963a) has pointed out. For these pleometrosis increases the effective population size, which compensates for loss of genetic variability consequent on inbreeding.

3. *Males as dispersal agents*

Wynne-Edwards (1962) has suggested that the congregations of males of social insects, particularly bees and wasps, that lack territorial dispersion mechanisms may serve to prevent overpopulation. It is suggested that they resemble the leks of some birds in being conspicuous groups of graded males which females visit to copulate with the top few. In birds these groups are well dispersed, it is thought by tradition, not all possible sites being used, though, of course, this is difficult to ascertain. In social insects where males are ephemeral some behavioural mechanism other than tradition would space the groups, such as a coalescence within male mobility range on a best object. This would be a system for males like that of aggregation and pleometrosis for females. The effect on the female population presumably would be to limit the number fertilized in an area to a quantity that did not lead to overpopulation. The difficulty is to see what relation the structure determining male grouping has to the resources on which the females depend.

Not enough evidence exists to settle the validity of this hypothesis. The circuits of *Bombus* already discussed are probably aggregated. They certainly overlap and stations are shared so that at any one a bee may appear every minute or so in good weather. As circuits are marked out each morning, plenty of opportunity for intraspecific reaction must occur, but little is known about this. Males of other social Hymenoptera which obviously aggregate into clusters may circuit, too, though this often only amounts to an oscillating movement. It can be seen in swarms of *Myrmica* males in Europe which form in the shelter of trees, houses, mountains, summits, and objects that stand out from the general level. Immediately against the marking object there is a dense cluster, some 20–25 cm in diameter, of rapidly and randomly circulating males. This breaks up periodically (usually with a gust of wind), but re-forms as males fly slowly with simple side-to-side orientation movements towards it. The high-density, high-activity zone near each marker is probably attractive to females and perhaps stimulatory, too. Such a system no doubt speeds sexual contact and it may enable the fittest males to predominate, as to endure the rigour and persistent activity that the congress provokes must demand considerable vitality. All available trees and peaks are not used and there is undoubtedly a tendency to collect round the most prominent. However, in treeless country even stone walls and buildings may be used and it is likely that only very uniform plains would be rendered uninhabitable. So the tendency to select the best of a set of objects within a perceptive field may lead simultaneously to reduced delay in sexual contact, selection of the best males for copulation, and dispersal, though the relevance of this last to the resources used by the females is obscure.

Neither the swarms of the ant *Pheidole sitarches* described by Wilson (1951) nor those of *Araucomyrmex tener* described by Weber (1963a) showed any tendency to coalesce, and several existed close together or even touching. Though they were probably orientating on some ground pattern, they do not seem to have been able to identify a best part of it and they can hardly have had very much dispersing effect, though quite probably they reduced the effective number of males by a factor of some 10^2 or 10^3 and offered the best to the females, who were easily able to find them. In those species where clusters drift, like *Lasius*, though the two primary functions are still fulfilled dispersal in relation to resources cannot be. However, as Wynne-Edwards has pointed out, the territorial system of ants and termites may provide sufficient dispersion.

A recent example of the selective power of mating flights is shown by *Apis mellifera*, in which drones of the subspecies *adansonii* appear to be more successful in inseminating queens of European subspecies than their own drones. This is one of the factors leading to the spread of *adansonii* in South America (Nogueira-Neto, 1964).

The female of the ant *Pheidole sitarches* breaks her wings off on the ground under the swarm (by no means always the case with ants), which effectively limits the dispersal in a generation to the distance males will fly to a swarm, which will depend, in extreme cases, on the distribution of mating structures (Wilson, 1957).

CHAPTER 14

INTERSPECIFIC COMPETITION

Before going on to the main subject of this chapter some cases of the relations between interbreeding subspecies are considered.

With species, competition leads to segregation if they are sufficiently dissimilar and the environment is sufficiently heterogeneous. This process involves loss of population to both, a fact which provides a measure of their interaction and is used as a definition of competition by Pontin (1961b, 1963). After segregation by these means those individuals of the population that are able to locate and establish themselves in this zone will be more likely to survive and leave progeny than others, and an evolution of discriminatory behaviour leading to direct segregation without interaction can be envisaged. In any event, species segregation into optimal zones increases the functional differentiation of the ecosystem and perhaps given suitable integration at higher energy levels improves its efficiency.

The ideas advanced by Hamilton (1964a and b) indicate that females that are closely related should co-operate readily and that hostility should increase with genetic dissimilarity at least as long as a gene pool is shared, that is, as long as interbreeding occurs. Genetic discontinuity once achieved there is more to gain by avoiding friction and reaching an accommodation; for these reasons one would expect subspecies to interact fiercely and species less so or hardly at all.

A. SUBSPECIFIC RELATIONS

The fierce hostility between subspecies of *Apis mellifera* has already been mentioned. Kalmus (1941) showed that Caucasian and Italian forms trained to the same dish of syrup fought when it dried up. Whichever got a start in exploiting the source could hold it by establishing an overwhelming population. In 1956 the African subspecies, *Apis mellifera adansonii*, was introduced into Brazil and has since spread very rapidly, in part naturally, in part with human help (Nogueira-Neto, 1964). They are a very hard-working, small, but extremely vicious form that swarm frequently and often establish themselves in termite mounds, a factor which is thought to help their spread substantially in an area in which the normal nesting sites are already occupied by two European subspecies (*mellifera* and *ligustica*). They interbreed, but their aggressive-ness and their swarming tendency appear to be genetically dominant and are not being diluted. Their drones, as has been pointed out, are also more successful. Actual conflict has not been described and it would seem possible that *adansonii* may be able to establish themselves safely by virtue of a better ability to exploit the habitat and the posses-sion of dominant genes, though they do appear to be well equipped for offence.

The fire-ant *Solenopsis saevissima richteri* Forel landed in Alabama, U.S.A., in 1918 and soon afterwards a small reddish form appeared, perhaps a second introduction. They interbred and a population ex-plosion followed (Wilson, 1951, 1953a). Nevertheless by 1949 the red form persisted and had replaced the dark one over most of the area except the coastal strips and a few inland patches. The warmth of the Gulf States is thought to have favoured the red form. This trend con-tinued in 1957 (Wilson and Brown, 1958). It is suggested that success depended partly on the red form's superior ability to find and destroy the young queens and colonies of the dark form.

Two subspecies of *Myrmica ruginodis* differing in methods of reproduc-tion were found together in western Scotland (Brian and Brian, 1949, 1955). One, though often starting colonies by groups of queens, never added any more later and its queens were large and able to found colonies alone (*macrogyna*, M); the other (*microgyna*, m) regularly added queens which were small and quite dependent on entering a colony (Weir, 1958). Intermediates were rare, though they did occur. The degree of reproductive contact was low, on account of low mutual attraction, but largely because the differing reproductive methods adapted the subspecies to differing habitats that were spatially apart and had different microclimates which led to sexual maturation at different times. Also m appeared to produce sexuals cyclically every few years whereas M produced them each year. M were able by means of their independent queens to detect newly created sites (such as felled woodland), but m were able to spread slowly but surely over stable plagioclimaxes. When they met they were hostile and the evidence indicated that m could prevent the intrusion of M. Hence they co-existed with eco-differentiation. Collingwood (1958a and b, 1959) has since obtained evidence that m is characteristic of north-western and M of south-eastern Britain. The latter zone is richer in ants with great com-petitive ability, such as *Lasius* species, and it is not surprising that only the mobile subspecies survives. This could well have been an important factor in the divergence of the two forms from a single prototype, like the congeneric *Myrmica rubra* L., which has large queens that both found colonies alone, in groups and by re-entering established colonies, and which persists locally in the south-east of Britain. Should such a form have colonized suitably permanent areas and attained high densities it is highly probable that, as already discussed, the positive selection for queen size would cease and be replaced by a selection for re-entry towards which size may contribute nothing. Given time and sufficient isolation, there seems no reason why such a form should not have evolved.

Indeed, there is evidence that this step in evolution is being taken and has been taken in a number of related species of ant. Thus *Formica sanguinea* has two modes of life in western Siberia, one with solitary colonies that are hostile to all others and have large strongly coloured workers, the other with groups of nests, not hostile and small less strongly marked workers which contract into a few bigger nests in winter (Marikovsky, 1963). Also, *Formica pallidefulva* Latreille has a subspecies *nitidiventris* Emery which is haplometrotic and another *incerta* Emery that is pleometrotic and buds (Talbot, 1948). In the *Formica rufa* group of Europe full species status is now given to what were earlier regarded as subspecies and varieties (Lange, 1956, 1957, 1958a and b, 1959, 1960). *F. rufa* itself is only mildly pleometrotic and can be single-queened, though they are temporary social parasites of *F. fusca*, whereas *F. polyctena* is wholly and highly pleometrotic and buds daughter colonies to the number of 65 or so covering several ha (Raignier, 1948). Though little syrup is exchanged between these buds (Chauvin, 1964), workers, especially nurses, are transported by foragers in spring and autumn, which no doubt helps to maintain unity (Marikovsky, 1962b; Kneitz, 1964). Furthermore, *F. rufa* is more sporadically distributed than *F. polyctena*, which is confined to especially favourable areas (Gösswald, 1942). Writing of this species complex, Marikovsky (1962b) says that the "colonial form" probably requires specially favourable conditions to establish itself and is always found at high population densities. Their colonies appear to start in more or less ant-free areas as single mounds of large workers that are hostile to all neighbouring ones. As the mounds grow the workers get smaller and buds are emitted if space allows. Though this may be a phenotypic effect, it could also arise from social parasitization of, say, *F. rufa* by *F. polyctena*, or again from a genetic deterioration in the size of supplementary queens. Marikovsky says that biometric studies revealed many transitional states, and he is of the opinion that they represent different methods of social organization designed to deal with different phases of the exploitation of a habitat. Otto (1960) found both species were more variable in number of queens than had been thought, and the presence of large workers in *F. rufa* colonies gave the frequency distribution of worker size a marked skewness. Using this he developed a discriminant function that predicted queen number. *F. ulkei*, like *Myrmica rubra*, appears to combine both features (Scherba, 1958).

It may well be that the difference in biology of *Oecophylla longinoda* in East and West Africa is due to similar causes (Ledoux, 1950; Way, 1953, 1954a and b; Vanderplank, 1960).

Budding is restrictive and perhaps temporary social parasitism by the pleometrotic type on the haplometrotic one would remedy this, but there is no firm evidence of it. Indeed, it was shown that *Myrmica ruginodis macrogyna* refused *microgyna* queens, but this is not sufficient negative evidence, as acceptance at different times of year in different conditions may take place. The possibility of the evolution of *Psithyrus-Bombus* pairs from a single species of *Bombus* that regularly practised both foundation by single queens and by usurpers, through a stage when a southern subspecies regularly usurped when it overlapped the northern form, has been thoroughly explored by Richards (1927b) and has certain analogies to the ant situation. Thus, two types of difference occur at this level: one between degree of activity, skill, and adaptability (*Apis* and *Solenopsis*), and one between reproductive method (*Myrmica*, *Formica*, and *Oecophylla*). In the former case it seems that a large measure of replacement is proceeding; in the latter, habitat segregation which is spatial as between stable and transient systems, and seral in those of the latter that succeed in stabilizing.

B. SPECIFIC RELATIONS

Long ago Sladen (1912) speculated on the relation between *Bombus terrestris* L. and *B. lucorum*, which overlap in range in England and perhaps hybridize slightly. The former is more southerly in general distribution, larger, more alert and aggressive and regularly usurps nests of *B. lucorum* if they are available, as it emerges from hibernation slightly later. Despite this the *lucorum* survives, especially to the north and in mountains. Methods of avoiding competition are frequently noted in this genus: thus *B. lapidarius* L. hibernates in shaded banks, whereas *B. terrestris* does so under trees. The difference in height at which male *Bombus* make their circuits has already been mentioned; *hypnorum* on the ground, *agrorum* and *pratorum* L. at bush height, *terrestris* and *lucorum* at herb height, and *lapidarius* on trees (Haas, 1949). However, this does not preclude aggregation into suitable zones, as in the case of Cumber's (1953) record of 7 species nesting in one refuse dump of area 0·8 ha where they had 38 nests.

A. D. Brian (1957) has studied the interrelations of 4 species of this genus in west Scotland and found many differences that reduce competition. Two species (*Bombus agrorum* (*a*) and *B. pratorum* (*p*)) tended to live and feed near woodland and scrub, and it is known that they nest on the soil surface and even in bushes (*p*) and their males circuit at bush height. Another two (*B. hortorum* L. (*h*) and *B. lucorum* (*l*)) went into more open places and nested underground (gaining in that way the necessary protection from trampling and weather), and *l* males are known to circuit at herb height. There was thus a basic difference in structural requirements, though this is easy to exaggerate.

Feeding was also different, not very much on account of the difference in habitat, though such facts as the preponderance of ericaceous pollen and the pollen of *Potentilla erecta* L. in the larval meconia of *l* support this (A. D. Brian, 1951), but more on account of differences in the tongue length of the bees. Of the woodland ones *a* had a longer tongue than *p*; of the others *h* had a very long tongue and *l* a short one. *l* and *p* frequented flowers with short corollas that also happen to be regular in shape and green to white or yellow in colour, whereas *a* and *h* frequented longer corolled flowers that are often irregular, red, blue, or purple. The mechanism of this connection is still unknown, though some light has been thrown on it (A. D. Brian, 1957). The bees collected pollen from the same flowers as nectar, only *l* and *p* regularly collecting from nectarless flowers. *l* in particular was a more versatile feeder than the others, for it cut its way into long-corolled flowers and collected honey-dew. In spite of these differences the species competed for food. A tendency for bees to settle on others in flowers was noticed which led to considerable and disturbing movement at high densities. *p* was particularly aggressive and dislodged *a*, but not *l*. *a* might be attacked in the air and hit to the ground and there is little doubt that groups of flowers were monopolized in this way. This led to a succession from *p* to *a* in plants that both foraged, for *p* starts and ends earlier in the year than *a*. Competition for structures was not investigated.

Vespula has been studied comparatively by Kemper (1961) and by Kemper and Döhring (1962). The *Paravespula* group are known to be more advanced socially than the *Dolichovespula* group and they have much bigger, stronger, and more differentiated nests and are more versatile feeders. Two species of *Paravespula*, *P. germanica* and *P. vulgaris* that coexist over a large area showed no significant complementarity, though the former had rather larger colonies than the latter and might perhaps as a result be more restricted in nest site. This pair warrant further detailed study.

The native honey-bee of Japan *Apis cerana* (*c*) is being replaced by the introduced European *A. mellifera* (*m*), both in apiaries and mountain areas where they live wild. Sakagami (1959) found that the workers of *m* were better at recognizing *c* even in the brood stage and were extremely hostile. In individual fighting *m* was stronger in all respects except its jaws and could prevent *c* using its sting. *m* was able to monopolize syrup dishes to which both were trained. In mixed apiaries, especially in autumn, both species rob each other, but whereas *m* builds up a large-scale attack to which *c* responds by evacuation, *c* only destroys weak colonies of *m*. The escape reaction of *c* is probably an adaptation to attack by the hornet *Vespa mandarinia* Smith, for *m*, which does not show it, is frequently massacred. This with the fact that it overwinters better appears to be the only two advantages that *c* enjoys. *m* is protected by man, is discriminating, strong, aggressive, and co-operative and is reputed to be a better forager, too. Presumably as long as man persists *m* will extend its range until the cold of the mountains becomes a critical factor in overwintering, unless perhaps the stronger jaws that *c* uses to enlarge its nest sites give it a greater potentiality in wild forest conditions.

A comparable study of *Apis dorsata* and *A. florea* has been started by Thakar and Tonapi (1961, 1962). The former is, of course, larger and nests higher up in trees, but both are highly migratory.

The many congeneric ant species that have been studied will be treated for convenience from boreal to tropical regions. *Myrmica* has been studied in western Scotland by Brian (1952b, 1955, 1956b). *M. scabrinodis* (*s*) is well known to live in shorter denser turf than *M. ruginodis* (*r*) (Diver, 1940). In Scotland the former also lives in bare areas in heather moor and is more common in stumps than *r*. Evidence was obtained that both are, in fact, attracted by the same warm soil and wood of such places, but that *s* drives *r* out after a period of siege, especially during dry or cold weather. *s* proved to be better adapted to areas where the sun reaches the soil surface, thus it makes small-chambered, soil-rich nests and is itself resistant to desiccation, and it stays in its nests all winter and summer except in severe drought and it forages near the soil surface. *r* on the other hand is adapted to longer, sparser vegetation, thus it builds light, larger-chambered nests high into the herb layer, incorporating much vegetation; it is not particularly resistant to desiccation; it readily leaves its nest in extreme weather or if shaded or pressed from other ants, and its long legs and greater agility fit it for moving in herbage.

And so, in competition, *s* through better adaptation and through better offensive skill is able to exclude *r* from the areas of greatest soil surface warmth, but it nevertheless survives very well in areas where the warmest zone is in the herb layer. In patchy vegetation the same differentiation occurs but foraging areas overlap, *r* foraging in a stratum above *s*. As captured *r* (even males) are eaten, the relationship is to some extent predatory as well as competitive. This transition from competition to predation is not open to phytophagous groups (like bees).

Some authors argue that if an animal is eaten it is predated, but this is too simple. True predation presumes that the prey is not competing with the predator for food resources. If it is, then its consumption is merely the best way of disposing of it and minimizing the loss of resources it has caused.

Two species of *Lasius* may occur together in English neutral grassland. *L. flavus* is pre-eminent as a mound builder and quite independent of special nesting structures, provided the grass is not too lank or of unsuitable composition (as already pointed out). It forages mainly beneath the surface and consumes a great variety of soil animals as well as cultivating many aphids for honeydew and prey (Pontin, 1958, 1961a). *L. niger* by contrast depends on stumps or stones or really bare soil in which to nest, forages to a considerable extent above ground in the herb and shrub stratum, especially on other species of ant, and it also cultivates many types of aphids and other bugs probably merely for honeydew; it is a more versatile feeder and is much more eurytopic and aggressive. Where nest sites are available in grassland it can establish itself and attain equilibrium with *L. flavus* populations, both increasing the distance apart of their nests and reducing their sexual production (Pontin, 1961b, 1963). Apart from taking food from the *L. flavus* it also undoubtedly eats them, so that the relationship is a complex mixture of competition and predation with no very profound similarity to the *Myrmica* situation, but it illustrates how a sparse supply of nest sites can leave sufficient room between a dominant species (*L. niger*) for a subordinate one (*L. flavus*) to exist. In practice they feed differently, but in theory they could feed identically. An extremely interesting feature of this relationship is that *L. flavus* uses stones on the surface as mechanical supports for nest soil, not for their heating properties as *L. niger* does, and in so doing covers them over and deprives *L. niger* of nest sites. On the other hand, as Marikovsky (1965) has pointed out, *Lasius niger* may use *L. flavus* mounds as nest site and food source combined.

The relations between the slave-making *Formica sanguinea* (*s*) and *F. rufa* (*r*) in the forests of western Siberia have been noted by Marikovsky (1963). He transplanted *r* nests into *s* areas. The former soon established an offensive either directly or from a specially constructed base-nest near the *r*, and began taking the pupae. To this the *r* reacted by evacuating with as much brood as possible, but the *s* went on to attack the workers and annihilate them. According to Marikovsky this is the pattern adopted in slave-raiding *F. fusca* and *F. rufibarbis* Fabricius, except that less hostility is shown to the workers of the slave species, though they may nevertheless be destroyed. Some of the pupae were taken back undamaged and yielded *r* workers. These were integrated, made characteristic nests and usually refused their own queens. A few that accepted *r* queens did not escape entirely from the *s* influence and were still visited by *s* workers which took food. The aggression of *s* increased if food and slave supplies were poor.

Dobrzanski (1961) noted in work in Poland that only small colonies of *F. rufa* and *F. pratensis* are successfully attacked by *F. sanguinea*; most of the pupae are eaten, but a few surplus give slaves.

Marikovsky (1963) also noticed that *F. sanguinea* could not only eliminate their slave species, but clear out others as well: *Lasius niger*, *L. flavus* and *Camponotus herculeanus* are mentioned. They then survived alone, feeding presumably in a general way on insects other than ants and perhaps tending aphids. This suggests that they have evolved from a stage when they eliminate other species as competitors, consuming those killed in the process, towards a stage of controlled predation, when they take pupae periodically, but do not destroy the prey colony, which in its turn has evolved defensive behaviour and avoids provoking *s* unduly, an example of the well-known phenomenon of mutual adaptation. Combined with the predator-prey relation is the host-slave one which alone endures in *Polyergus rufescens* (Dobrzanski, 1965). Colonial forms of *Formica rufa* (possibly *F. polyctena*) bud colonies and spread out in Siberian forest, displacing most other species as they go. *F. fusca* is destroyed completely.

Formica truncorum and *F. fusca* were negatively correlated in grassland on Mt. Hakkôda in Japan (Yasuno, 1964) and *Camponotus herculeanus* was associated with the former. *F. truncorum* forms clusters of nests that exclude other species and are distributed mainly in the marginal forest-grass zone. *F. fusca* nests between these.

Solenopsis saevissima richteri, whose subspecific problems have already been discussed, comes into contact with two native congeners: *S. xyloni* McCook and *S. geminata* Fabricius (see Wilson, 1951). Towards these it has been extremely hostile and the first is almost eliminated, probably because being a grassland species it was too similar to survive. The second, though previously eurytopic, is now confined to woodland, where it finds refuge from *S. saevissima*, but a light colour form has been lost in the process, so that a species initially variable genetically and ecologically has through interaction with a congeneric immigrant become restricted in both these senses (Brown and Wilson, 1956).

The relation between two species of *Anoplolepis*, both immigrant, have been noted by Way (1953). *A. longipes* (*l*) occupied an area round Zanzibar in which there were two isolated patches of *A. custodiens* (*c*). The former is less aggressive and is noticeably deterred when entering *c* territory. Way saw an advance by *c* into an *l* zone during which *l* were driven off and killed. Writing some 7 years later, Vanderplank (1960) recalls that *c* has occupied about 1 600 ha of *l* territory. The comparative ecology of these two species should be studied.

The interspecific relations of nomadic army ants are particularly interesting. *Eciton* is a genus that has been extensively studied in tropical America by Schneirla and his associates (summarized Schneirla, 1957) and by Rettenmeyer (1963). Most information concerns *E. hamatum* (*h*) and *E. burchelli* (*b*). The latter is more versatile than *h* and has bigger populations. They are both epigaeic, but *b* tolerates more light, raids higher in trees and forms arboreal bivouacs (for which the long claws of the workers adapt them) which have a higher central temperature, due no doubt in part to the larger colony size. *b* has a more highly organized raiding pattern, with a mass of workers in front instead of a number of branching columns, and direct liaison is maintained over a wider area (instead of individually through the basal column). Thus when prey is discovered they are able to mass more quickly. The workers are individually larger, more active, more agile, and they bite more strongly and sting more virulently. They have a rushing attack and execute quick, excited, darting movements. As a result of this individual and group superiority *b* catch more food of a wider variety including adult arthropods and ants of other species, though many no doubt escape, especially if they remain still; indeed, Rettenmeyer believes that *b* are selective feeders as are some African army ants (Wheeler, 1922b). The slower probing attack of *h* results in a greater proportion of brood stages being eaten (compare wasps and other ants). A third species, *E. vagans* Oliv., which raids at ground level kills more ants than the other two. In general there is a correlation between prey size and the size of the *Eciton* worker. Thus variation in individual size and activity, in group organization, and in foraging method and stratum foraged, lead to a variation in food, so that in the same area different species catch different prey, and this presumably is the basis of their overlap.

A similar relation appears to exist between African army ants (Raignier and van Boven, 1955). *Dorylus* (*Anomma*) *wilverthi* (*w*) has larger more active and excitable workers than *D.* (*A*) *nigricans* (*n*). It sends out more raids which are bigger and a greater proportion of workers bring back prey that are probably larger on the average. Though both raid partly underground, *w* is less hypogaeic than *n*. Both nest underground, but *w* forms a compact mass in a single central cavity near the surface (1–2 m deep), which gives a higher temperature and a shorter interval between emigrations. Unlike *Eciton*, these forms include vertebrates in their diet. *w*, in fact, compares with *n* rather as *E. burchelli* compared with *E. hamatum*. Different species of *Dorylus* do not appear to show hostility; they simply avoid each other and their coexistence depends presumably on differences in the nature of their food.

Attine ants are characteristically non-aggressive (Weber, 1958) and several species of one genus may live close together without interference. This is rather surprising in view of the fact that they must collect vegetable debris at some periods for their fungus gardens.

Generalization is not easy. *Bombus* species have many small differences in behaviour and individual structure that affect their demands on the crucial limiting resources of food and structure, and tend to reduce competition, but not eliminate it. A key species, dominant, vigorous, and versatile, literally keeps the others in their places partly directly, partly through a hierarchy.

Ants, being primarily soil-inhabiting apterous insects, have found stratification of foraging zones and to a less extent nesting zones an easy way of segregating; probably only a small change in reaction to light intensity is necessary. However, if combined with individual structural change, like extension of legs, claws, pigmentation, or simply size, and with degree of social organization, it can lead to big food differences, as are so strikingly shown by Dorylinae, whose food ranges from inactive arthropods to small vertebrates.

An alternative way of segregating in ants is the tendency to emphasize offensive rather than architectural skill. This enables one species to dominate an area in an ecosystem whilst the other extends more widely into less hospitable but equally productive parts, and leads perhaps in the end to the evolution of predator-prey relationships. In phytophagous forms like bees this, of course, is not possible, but social parasitism may be an alternative.

CHAPTER 15

INTERGENERIC COMPETITION

Competition between less closely related species is considered here. Hostility is considerable when such forms meet, but there are many ways of avoiding or reducing this contingency where major individual differences in size and structure as well as social organization and feeding method can occur. This subject leads to a consideration of the organization of the ant, bee, wasp, or termite community of an area.

A well-known example in Europe is the competition between the honey-bee (*Apis mellifera*) and wild bees, particularly species of *Bombus*, for food. This is reduced by various factors. First, the honey-bee has a short tongue compared with most *Bombus*, and only visits open short-corolled flowers except when it uses the holes bitten by *B. lucorum* in flowers whose nectaries are otherwise inaccessible (e.g. *Trifolium pratense*), a curious instance of a bee helping its competitor. Honey-bees are also much more restricted by climatic conditions in foraging (reviewed A. D. Brian, 1954), though in the relatively short diurnal period of activity they are able to deploy a much bigger foraging force far more efficiently and, moreover, they certainly dominate *Bombus* on flowers. This is thus another case of a species that is highly efficient, versatile, and dominant in a restricted zone of the total space-time habitat, but which leaves plenty of scope for others elsewhere.

The two *Myrmica* species that inhabit acidic grassland in Scotland and have been discussed are part of a larger ant fauna that includes *Leptothorax acervorum* (also Myrmicinae) and *Formica lemani* (Formicinae). These two are both restricted by their inability to construct mounds, for they can only excavate and must therefore live under bare surfaces, usually in dead wood, or under large flat stones. If these are sparse, as is frequently the case, large gaps are left in the food supply for exploitation by *Myrmica* (cf. *Lasius niger* in relation to *L. flavus* in neutral grassland). Large old tree stumps were colonized by all four species at first (giving an aggregated distribution) and until the dominant *Formica lemani* drove the others off a zonation in relation to insolation quota was detectable: *F. lemani* (south), *M. scabrinodis* (south-east) and *M. ruginodis* (elsewhere but mainly north-east). *L. acervorum* alone were able to bore fine galleries into the harder wood, where they were safe from attack (as Elton and Miller, 1954, observed elsewhere). The feeding of *F.*

lemani did not wholly conflict with the *Myrmica* feeding: they foraged higher, into shrubs, over much larger areas, and were able to catch and carry individually much larger prey; and their peak activity was midday in bright, warm weather instead of early and late in dull weather. Here, then, is yet another example of a restricted dominant form leaving space for subordinates.

Myrmica scabrinodis meets *Lasius flavus* in various parts of England, and they appear to have established a predator-prey relationship, for this *Myrmica* is often found living on *Lasius* mounds, feeding on their workers. Waloff and Blackith (1962) have recorded some mounds destroyed in this way and Marikovsky (1965) has described a variety of ant species attacking *Lasius flavus*. Paraschivescu (1963), on the other hand, has stressed the ability of this species to defend itself. Restriction caused by nest-site specificity in ants has been remarked on by Hayashida (1959) in his survey of the ant fauna of Mt. Atusanupuri, an active volcano in Hokkaido where each species has a characteristic nest site that is less flexible than the foraging area. In the study of ants on Mt. Hakkôda already mentioned Yasuno (1963, 1964) found circumstantial evidence that *Formica fusca* restricted *Myrmica ruginodis* to woodland (almost as *F. lemani* does in Scotland). He also stressed the importance of worker size to coexistence and pointed out that three species with small workers (*Tetramorium caespitum*, *Pheidole fervida* Smith, and *Paratrechina flavipes* F. Smith) and three with large (*Formica truncorum*, *F. fusca*, and *Camponotus herculeanus* Mayr) appeared to be distributed independently. The possible importance of two sizes has been commented on by Golley and Gentry (1964) in relation to old field systems in America, where the large *Pogonomyrmex badius* and the small *Dorymyrmex* occur together. Another example is where the dominant ants of the *Formica rufa* group force the smaller *Lasius niger* and *Myrmica rubra* to live underground like *Lasius flavus*, and they lose many sexuals at nuptial time (Marikovsky, 1962b). Way (1954a), too, has recorded that *Oecophylla*, which is notorious for clearing its trees of insect life, leaves small colonies of small ants of the genera *Cardiocondyla* and *Tapinoma*, which nests in cracks in trunks and fruits; and Rettenmeyer (1963a) has remarked that *Eciton* is not hostile to smaller species of ant and will share trails with *Atta*. This process is carried to its logical conclusion when the small ants nest in the large ones' nests and even share their galleries (*Solenopsis*, *Leptothorax*, and others).

The world movements of *Pheidole megacephala* Fabricius and *Iridomyrmex humilis* have been charted (see Haskins, 1945; Goetsch, 1951; Elton, 1958), and it is generally agreed that each has a variety of advantages, economic and military, over the indigenous forms they have replaced. *Iridomyrmex*, for example, is a very versatile feeder, very pleometrotic, semi-nomadic, and able to use human transport for dispersal as well as being outstandingly well equipped for offence. In the Gulf states of North America, however, it is now limited to urban areas by another invader, *Solenopsis saevissima*, already mentioned, which lives in rural areas (Wilson, 1951), but exactly what the basis of this segregation is does not appear to be known.

The ant fauna and its interactions in orchards near Zanzibar has been described by Way (1953, 1954a and b) and Vanderplank (1960). So far the relations of two *Anoplolepis* species have been described. The principal ant is *Oecophylla longinoda* (O), that makes leaf nests in the crowns with larval saliva, many in each tree. It occurs wherever the vegetation is rich enough and keeps its tree territories remarkably clear of other ant species. But it can be exterminated by *Anoplolepis longipes* (A), an immigrant. The O collect at the base of the trees in defensive formation, but can be picked up and carried away, or if they try to escape they are cornered and sprayed with poison in a bite wound which immobilizes them in a few minutes, after which they are taken to the nest. Further defensive groups are made round their nests, but the A advance is not stemmed. The latter species only appear to be limited by their need to nest in bare soil, which makes it likely that they will only replace O locally, another example of a dominant form that is nest-site limited. Way has suggested that the hostility of A is only aroused by aggressive species of ant such as O and *Dorylus* when raiding. *A. custodiens*— which is replacing *A. longipes* in the area— is, curiously enough, less effective in dealing with O, though it eventually succeeds through numerical superiority (Vanderplank, 1960).

A fourth species, *Pheidole punctulata* Mayr (P), interacts with these two in the trees. Its basic nest is in the foot of coconut palms, but it ascends to the crown and establishes subsidiary nests. Both O and A can usually prevent them ascending, but where the former is unable to do so distinct territorial boundaries that can only be transgressed with much hostility occur. The balance between these two is evidently rather delicate, for Way records that P can destroy isolated queens of O and small colonies in artificial circumstances, though only at considerable loss to themselves. Vanderplank (1960) records that P can destroy O in dry weather, but the situation is reversed in wet. P workers grasp O individuals and soldiers dismember them. Clearly where a balance is delicate the establishment and regulation of boundaries, as in the tree crown, is advantageous to both.

Vanderplank records a species of *Crematogaster* that immobilizes O workers and then leaves them instead of taking them back to the nest and eating them, an unusual case in ants of interference pure and simple.

Though successful interaction depends on offensive skill, there can be no doubt, especially in the case of P and O, that the necessary basis is adaptation. O is highly adapted to the forest or orchard life, as it is even independent of the soil for nesting, and has in addition mutualistic relations of considerable refinement with species of *Saissetia* (Way, 1954b, 1963). On clove trees O has six species of Coccidae not used by A or P, though these use various free-living species, and A cultivates a *Rastrococcus* that is rarely associated with O. When O is displaced its bugs are not taken over. Way has suggested that these differences in bug culture may assist segregation between O and P in the crown.

A similar community has been studied in the Solomon Islands by Brown (1959), especially in coconut plantations. The four main species were *Oecophylla smaragdina* Emery, *Pheidole megacephala*, *Anoplolepis longipes*, and *Iridomyrmex myrmecodiae* Emery. The last of these is like *Oecophylla* arboreal, and indigenous. Brown noted a succession in some areas of *Pheidole* (P) to *Oecophylla* (O) to *Anoplolepis* (A). The former he regarded as characteristic of unstable ant communities; it often died out from intrinsic causes and was replaced by many indigenous forms with small colonies before these were finally driven off by O. Quite frequently this last species formed islands in areas predominantly inhabited by A or P, and in these cases the O might be restricted to the tree crowns, though why the O were not entirely dislodged is unknown. In fighting O, P frequently advanced under the cover of old termite runways, and colony boundaries were often well marked and fairly stable (cf. Way).

In outline the community structure in these equatorial forests and orchards thus resembles that in Scottish acid grassland, for in each case the dominant ant, skilled offensively, is limited by nest-site specificity and in other minor ways, and so leaves space in which two others establish a delicate equilibrium with imperfect stratification of nesting and feeding partly achieved by interactive and partly by selective processes. In other cases small ants exist in the heart of the others.

Iridomyrmex (I) is pleometrotic and forms pure blocks with clearly defined margins. It is intolerant of other ants and like O goes for the crowns, thus making any stratification out of the question. Brown noted that it was frequently found in zones rich in epiphytes and creepers, the former myrmecophytic, the latter giving leaf shelters, and showed that it was dependent on habitat structure for nesting and defensive operations (unlike O), which no doubt limited its spread. In defence they massed at the base of the tree trunks, and Brown took the view that successful offence depended largely on numbers and that species which were well adapted to the situation established large populations and could expend more of these in expanding the area foraged. In such situations the advantage of a permanent pleometrotic system is clear.

Human interference had certainly disturbed and simplified the ecosystem in these studies. In tropical rain forest in New Guinea, however, Wilson (1959a) found 172 species of 59 genera. They were stratified, most living in the soil and in pieces of rotting wood, some in shrubs (the least common) and many in trees, where they made silk or carton nests or lived in epiphytes, twigs and branches, all available nesting sites being used. Foraging tended to proceed downwards. Wilson found that feeding was quite specialized even amongst predators, and the picture emerged of the coexistence of a complex, highly interspersed mixture of specialists. This presumably is the logical conclusion to prolonged stability.

Noirot (1959) is of the opinion that competition between species and less close taxa is an important factor limiting termite numbers. Fighting involving workers and soldiers is often recorded, yet several species may coexist, perhaps only temporarily, in a log, with galleries intertwining. Noirot (1960) has described how in savannah near the Ivory Coast (now Ghana) of Africa whilst *Bellicositermes natalensis* has been decreasing *Amitermes evuncifer* Silv. has been increasing, though the situation has not been analysed and a succession might be all that is involved. However, the latter may actively eject the former, and it certainly enters dead nests before they have eroded and crumbled, as well as displacing *Cubitermes* and *Trinervitermes* from their nests (the latter resisting more effectually). In other parts of Africa, *B. natalensis* and *A. evuncifer* occur together. Sands (1961), writing of the nest of *Trinervitermes ebenerianus*, says that it consists of a framework of curving floors and pillars (characteristic of the genus) rather than the usual system of chambers and tunnels. This, he suggests, may well enable it to share mounds with other species by forming complementary structures that leave little space between.

Ants, bees, and wasps frequently interact in their search for sugars, but the former rarely seem to protect flowers from bees, an interesting exception being *Oecophylla*, which captures, and kills for eating, many *Apis mellifera* (Way, 1954a). Wasps are restricted to very open flowers by the shortness of their tongue and perhaps obtain more sugar from fruit and honeydew (especially *Paravespula*). In the coniferous forests of Germany, *Formica rufa* group ants and *Apis mellifera* both collect honeydew. More aphids are found in trees near the ants' nests and, as the bees collect honeydew that is surplus to the ants' requirements (from leaves and on hot days when the ants retire), the yield of honey from ant-inhabited forests is 1·6 times as great as from ant-free ones (Wellenstein, 1958a and b, 1959, 1960; Buchner, 1959). The ants collect it directly, of course, and are able to keep bees away by shooting poison at them.

It is interesting in this connection to note that the *Formica rufa* group of ants reduce various pine and spruce sawfly populations, especially near their nests. This does not reduce the birds (which eat these insects) and may even increase them, for it is thought that they may eat ants, too, though reluctantly (Bruns, 1957, 1959, 1960b, 1961). Of course, unattractive foods form valuable reserves.

Thus the large differences that can occur between species of different genera or families increase the possibility of segregation, though, of course, they open the path to a certain amount of convergence, too. Big variations in size and major differences in feeding and nesting habit are possible. The existence of dominance hierarchies demonstrated for the Scottish ant community suggests a possible way in which the well-known negative binomial distribution relating species and individual numbers could be generated, rather on the lines that Clark *et al.* (1964) have suggested using human society as a model.

CHAPTER 16

PREDATORS AND PARASITES

It has already been emphasized that much competition can be regarded as predation, particularly amongst ants that are usually polyphagous. Gause (1934) did, of course, class predation as a form of competition. It is not intended to make a list of species that eat social insects here, merely to record a few recent quantitative observations and interactions; ant enemies have been thoroughly summarized by Bequaert (in Wheeler, 1922b) and the enemies of *Bombus* by A. D. Brian (1954) and Free and Butler (1959), and termite predators have been discussed by Weesner (1960). Predation in the air and on the ground or in the nest will be distinguished for convenience.

A. ON THE GROUND AND IN THE NEST

1. *Bees and wasps*

Halictine bees are often attacked by Mutillid parasites, and Lin (1964) has recently described how they co-operate in defence and has reviewed the literature on this subject. *Halictus duplex* is attacked by three species of ant, only one of which (*Formica fusca*) certainly enters the nest whilst the inhabitants are alive (Sakagami and Hayashida, 1961).

Bombus suffer in all stages of their life cycle from a variety of vertebrate and invertebrate enemies any one of which could operate a density-dependent controlling relationship. The hibernating queens and the young colonies are particularly susceptible, the latter especially as they are left unguarded when the queen forages. Sladen (1912) made a number of observations on this, and recently Cumber (1953) found 21 % of 80 *B. agrorum* nests destroyed by rodents and badgers and this might well have been higher, but information on the very young nests is difficult to obtain. *Psithyrus*, the social parasitic bee, does not seem to have been studied quantitatively, though it prevents the reproduction of *Bombus* once it has usurped the colony; but the parasitic Nematode *Sphaerularia bombi* Duf. was found in 100/146 queens of *B. lucorum* by Cumber (1949b). Workers may be parasitized by conopid flies, and again Cumber has recorded a rate of 12 %. Attacks on the adults by the mite *Tarsonoemus* and the protozoan *Nosema* are not usually fatal.

Tachinid flies parasitize larvae, particularly, according to Cumber, where the nest entrance is rather conspicuous. Finally wax moths of various kinds may destroy the nest structure and even go on to eat the brood.

Apis mellifera is attacked in the hive by many organisms both predatory and parasitic, including diseases, though it is widely held that its defences are very effective. Weak colonies may be destroyed. Apart from many vertebrates, it is interesting in the present context that Vespid wasps can be very destructive. In warm climates, *Vespa* is the main genus concerned: *V. mandarinia* in Japan has already been discussed, and *V. orientalis* in Egypt may exterminate whole apiaries in late summer after the bees have stopped breeding (Wafa, 1956); and *V. cincta* Fabr. in India is just as damaging (Subbiah and Mahadeven, 1957). In cooler regions the genus *Vespula* is more important: *V. maculifrons* (Buysson), *V. vidua* (Sauss.) in N. America (Morse and Gary, 1961), and *V. vulgaris* L. and *V. germanica* F. in Europe. All these wasps attack most fiercely and in greatest numbers at the end of the season, after the bees have stopped breeding, and small colonies can often be eliminated. By putting a trap under the hive entrance Morse and Gary (1961) collected the bodies of a number of invaders, and apart from the wasps just mentioned they caught a good many bees of various genera that had presumably been attracted by the smell of honey.

Tropical wasps are attacked by doryline and other ants that remove all the brood. The wasps appear to be adapted to this, for they evacuate in a body and start another nest elsewhere, building it in only a few days (Richards and Richards, 1951). Protection from dorylines can be found in trees inhabited by another ant of the genus *Dolichoderus*, which does not interfere with the wasps (or with the birds which take refuge likewise).

A 2-year cycle in frequency of *Vespula* nests has been detected at Wisley in southern England over a period of 25 years by Fox-Wilson (1946). This suggests some form of control by predator or parasite: badgers, a parasite of the male called *Gordius*, and another parasite *Rhipiphorus* have all been suggested, but not confirmed. The genera *Vespula* and *Polistes* have, like *Bombus*, specific social parasites which might be able to exert a control over their populations locally (Richards, 1953).

2. *Ants and termites*

Distinctly predatory behaviour is shown by the myrmecophagous cerapachyine ants to which once again the prey species appear to be adapted in this case by the habit of passive hiding (Wilson, 1958b); and, of course, the dorylines are also predatory. Again *Oecophylla* predates straggling *Dorylus nigricans* workers at the rate of 600 an hour (Way, 1954a) and *Dorylus* will avoid even empty nests of this species (Ledoux, 1950). Over twelve species of ant have been found eating foundress queens of *Oecophylla* (Vanderplank, 1960). The number of species that feed on *Lasius flavus* has already been described. Social parasitism is very common in ants and must destroy many nests where these are numerous.

Many vertebrates eat ants, and it is not surprising that they are the vectors of cestode parasites whose main hosts are gallinaceous birds (Nelmes, 1938; Muir, 1954). Woodpeckers (Picidae), which pick ants from their nests in winter, have increased in Bavarian forests since the ants were protected (Gösswald, 1958). Ants are not very often afflicted with fungus diseases, probably as they groom so much (Wheeler, 1910), but in certain areas this does happen (reviewed Bequaert in Wheeler, 1922b; Marikovsky, 1962a).

Termites in the soil and wood are frequently eaten by ants, which have indeed evolved specialists for this purpose (Wheeler, 1936). Recently Williams (1959b) has described how *Cubitermes ugandensis* (Termitidae) die as a result of the raids of *Dorylus* (*Anomma*) *kohli* Wasmann, a hypogaeic army ant; a fungal parasite is also involved. Kalshoven (1959) has described how the tree-nesting *Neotermes tectonae* loses many young colonies to ants, more than to woodpeckers.

B. IN THE AIR

The sexual stages suffer most in the air, for workers of bees and wasps appear to be fairly immune to predation. The queen *Apis mellifera* during her pre-mating and mating flights is very exposed, and it has been suggested that males keep dragonflies and other possible predators from the mating places (Gary, 1963).

The nuptial flights of ants and termites attract many organisms that do not normally feed on insects at all. In addition wasps catch them and store them in their nests (Richards, 1953; Chapman, 1963) and many are eaten as they land by various ants. The interesting feature of these flights from the present point of view is whether this predation could control and stabilize the population. Large synchronous flights certainly attract more than small inconspicuous ones, but no data are available on the proportion eaten at different densities. Weesner (1960), discussing termites, takes the view that successful matings will be greater in massive flights in spite of heavy predation. Yet inconspicuous flights in which the females exercise a greater power of attraction over a distance could surely be as successful (as in *Formica*). Indeed, it is probably intermediate sizes that are unsatisfactory. One of the weaknesses of this predation as a control is that it is not reciprocal, for whereas the birds suppress the insects, these form only a small part of the bird's total food supply and can hardly be expected to react on them, unless perhaps they provide a food store that is critical for migration or hibernation.

So, although a great deal has been known for a long time about the type of enemies that face each group of social insect, and general ideas exist about their relative importance, there is a great need of accurate quantitative studies that assess mortality in relation to population density.

CHAPTER 17

POPULATION REGULATION

In this final chapter evidence regarding the nature of population control in the various groups is brought together. Bees and wasps, though of different trophic levels in the main, can be conveniently grouped, as they all fly and have quite specialized nesting requirements which usually lead to their nesting in clusters (a method with some advantages) and foraging freely in the surrounds. Termites and ants, of course, only walk, at least in their vegetative phase, have less specialized nesting requirements, and forage in a more or less guarded area around their nests. Again on the whole they belong to different trophic levels.

A. BEES AND WASPS

As bees are in the main primary consumers, it would be expected that they would not be limited by intraspecific competition for food, but in some other way, unless perhaps their food supply is not as great as it appears to be (Klomp, 1964; Voute, 1957; Huffaker, 1957).

Halictine bees do not appear to be limited by nesting area, for they restrict themselves to certain zones even when other similar ones are near by, and there are indications that parasites hold their numbers down, but not enough is known about their food supply, which may not always be distributed optimally in relation to the nesting zone.

Bombus is a well-worked genus. Many of the queens produced in the summer die during the winter, probably through predation and disturbance during hibernation, a density-dependent process. In spring they depend on rodent nests (and to a less extent bird nests), the supply of which is presumably related to the rodent population at some previous date (a classical problem), but the value of this is no doubt reduced by the current rodent density, as they both disturb and predate. Competition for these nest sites occurs. An interesting cause of spring mortality is the failure of co-ordination in spring between bee emergence and flower opening, but this cannot control the average population level (cf. caterpillars and leaf opening, Varley, 1963). During summer there is evidence of competition for food, and there are numerous predatory and parasitic influences that could hold the population down at least locally. Various investigators have provided nest boxes for these bees, often without success, and Medler (1957) found that the provision of nest boxes in north Wisconsin, where bees were already numerous, increased the population, but not in southern Wisconsin, where they were sparse. He suggests that in the north a greater area of natural woodland provides a good all-season food supply, but in the south, which is more agricultural, food is too sporadic and frequently limiting.

Apis mellifera is today domesticated and brought into a sort of host-ectoparasitic relationship with man, who controls its population density by varying the number of nest sites. Only where too many are put in one place (and they are usually clustered in apiaries) does food limitation reduce the size and number of colonies. How nest-site number is normally determined is a complex human sociological problem, but in the best areas (good forage and climate) population probably rises to a food limit. As with *Bombus*, an all-the-year supply that is adequate at the prevailing temperatures is needed. In primeval forests nest sites in old trees and rocks were almost certainly used, and no doubt the subject of much competition from many organisms. There would also no doubt be more predation and disease which could be transmitted during robbing or drift. Perhaps there is still time to make bionomic studies of wild colonies.

Wasps, as secondary consumers, might be limited by food supply, competition, or vertebrate predators. The last are probably responsible for a big loss of hibernating queens and young colonies in temperate Vespidae. There is also competition for nest sites that are no doubt created by soil vertebrates for the most part (as in *Bombus*, though the wasps are perhaps less exacting in their nest-site requirements). These same vertebrates may later interfere with the young nests. Fox-Wilson's 2-year cycle could arise in this way, though man, who competes with Vespids in late summer at food sources, is also likely to be implicated. The tropical Polybiinae appear to be limited by predatory interference as well, for they are often notably clustered in certain ant trees, though what controls the incidence of these is no doubt a complex problem.

B. TERMITES AND ANTS

These can excavate their own nests unaided, but their skill in doing so varies considerably, and many that are sound in other ways (economically and militarily) may be poor at nest making and are undoubtedly limited by this. Those that can build extend into cooler zones, and may leave the soil altogether, but can still be limited by the structural characteristics of the vegetation. Mating structures are likewise very much reduced in ants and termites, and there is no evidence that they limit population, though this is possible.

When nesting is easy self-spacing is apparent, and accomplished by various devices (territory, condensation, and pleometrosis), but little information exists as yet about the extent to which an optimal-sized territory related to the food supply of an area can be established. There is probably some competition for food, more perhaps in relation to plants for harbouring bugs than in relation to insect prey. Way (1963) has pointed out that steady states between bugs and ants might develop in *Lasius*, and if so the ants could be limited by intraspecific competition for food. He maintains that this does not happen with *Oecophylla*, whose food trees are not lacking, but whose availability is often blocked by other species of ants. This is certainly true of most of the species considered in this review.

It is because of this ground organization that the degree of predation of nuptial masses, though often extraordinarily great, may have no effect on the stable population level. On the ground predation and parasitization (social in particular) are difficult to assess. There are many organisms that eat workers, brood, and queens in the process of starting colonies, and in certain areas the common ant is highly subject to certain social parasites, but this is very local as a rule and the evidence indicates that more control is exercised by self-spacing and competition than by the other processes. This may not be so in termites, which have to contend with extensive ant predation.

REFERENCES

Adeli, E. (1962). *Z. angew. Ent.* **49**, 290–296. Zur Ökologie der Ameisen im Gebiet des Urwaldes Rotwald (Niederösterreich).

Allen, M. D., and Jeffree, E. P. (1956). *Ann. appl. Biol.* **44**, 649–656. The influence of stored pollen and of colony size on the brood rearing of honey-bees.

Allen, M. D., and Jeffree, E. P. (1957). *J. econ. Ent.* **50**, 211–212. The annual cycle of pollen storage by honey-bees.

Andrewartha, H. G., and Birch, L. C. (1954). "The Distribution and Abundance of Animals." University of Chicago Press, Chicago, Illinois.

Ayre, G. L. (1957). *Insectes sociaux* **4**, 173–176. Ecological notes on *Formica subnitens* (Creighton) (Hymenoptera, Formicidae).

Ayre, G. L. (1960). *Naturwissenschaften* **47**, 502–503. Der Einfluss von Insektennahrung auf das Wachstum von Waldameisenvöllkern.

Batra, S. W. T. (1964). *Insectes sociaux* **11**, 159–185. Behaviour of the social bee, *Lasioglossum zephyrum*, within the nest (Hymenoptera, Halictidae).

Bernard, F. (1961). *Bull. Soc. Hist. Nat. Afrique du Nord.* **52**, 21–40. Biotopes habituels des Fourmis Sahariennes de plaine, d'après l'abondance de leurs nids en 60 Stations très diverses.

Bingefors, S., Eskilsson, L., and Fridén, F. (1960). *Svensk. Frötidn.* **29**, 11–15. Insect populations and seed setting in seed clover in the Mälar-Hjälmar district, 1959.

Bitancourt, A. A. (1941). *Arch. Inst. Biol.* **12**, 229–236. Expressao matematica do crescimento de formigueiros de *Atta sexdens rubropilosa* representado pelo aumento do numero de olheiros.

Bodenheimer, F. S. (1937a). *Biol. Rev.* **12**, 393–430. Population problems of social insects.

Bodenheimer, F. S. (1937b). *Quart. Rev. Biol.* **12**, 406–425. Studies in Animal Populations. II. Seasonal population trends of the honey-bee.

Bodenheimer, F. S. (1958). *Monogr. Biol.* **6**, 276 pp. Animal ecology today. Dr W. Junk, Den Haag, Netherlands.

Bodenheimer, F. S., and Ben-Nerya, A. (1937). *Ann. appl. Biol.* **24**, 385–403. One-year studies on the biology of the honey-bee in Palestine.

Box, T. W. (1960). *Ecology* **41**, 381–382. Notes on the harvester ant, *Pogonomyrmex barbatus var. molefacieus*, in south Texas.

Bozina, K. D. (1961). *Pchelovodstvo* **38**, 13. How long does the queen live?

Brereton, J. Le Gay. (1962). Symposium of the Royal Society of Victoria, Melbourne 1959. Evolved regulatory mechanisms of population control.

Brian, A. D. (1951). *Ent. mon. Mag.* **87**, 207–212. Brood development in *Bombus agrorum*.

Brian, A. D. (1952). *J. Anim. Ecol.* **21**, 223–240. Division of labour and foraging in *Bombus agrorum* (Fabricius).

Brian, A. D. (1954). *Bee World* **35**, 61–67, 81–91. The foraging of bumble-bees.

Brian, A. D. (1957). *J. Anim. Ecol.* **26**, 71–98. Differences in the flowers visited by four species of bumble-bees and their causes.

+ Brian, M. V. (1950). *J. Anim. Ecol.* **19**, 119–123. The stable winter population structure in species of *Myrmica*.

Brian, M. V. (1951). *Physiol. comp. et oecol.* **2**, 248–262. Summer population changes of the ant *Myrmica*.

+ Brian, M. V. (1952a). *Ent. mon. Mag.* **88**, 84–88. Interaction between ant colonies at an artificial nest site.

+ Brian, M. V. (1952b). *J. Anim. Ecol.* **21**, 12–24. The structure of a dense natural ant population.

Brian, M. V. (1953a). *Physiol. comp. et oecol.* **3**, 25–36. Oviposition by workers of the ant *Myrmica*.

+ Brian, M. V. (1953b). *Physiol. Zoöl.* **26**, 355–366. Brood rearing in relation to worker number in the ant *Myrmica*.

Brian, M. V. (1954). *Insectes sociaux* **1**, 101–122. Studies of caste differentiation in *Myrmica rubra* (L). 1 — The growth of queens and males.

Brian, M. V. (1955). *J. Anim. Ecol.* **24**, 336–351. Food collection by a Scottish ant community.

Brian, M. V. (1956a). *Physiol. Zoöl.* **29**, 173–194. Group form and causes of working inefficiency in the ant *Myrmica rubra* (L.).

Brian, M. V. (1956b). *Insectes sociaux* **3**, 474–487. The natural density of *Myrmica rubra* and associated ants in West Scotland.

Brian, M. V. (1956c). *J. Anim. Ecol.* **25**, 339–347. Exploitation and interference in interspecies competition.

Brian, M. V. (1956d). *J. Anim. Ecol.* **25**, 319–337. Segregation of species of the ant genus *Myrmica*.

+ Brian, M. V. (1957a). *Insectes sociaux* **4**, 177–190. The growth and development of colonies of the ant *Myrmica*.

Brian, M. V. (1957b). *Insectes sociaux* **4**, 191–210. Serial organization of brood in *Myrmica*.

Brian, M. V. (1957c). *Physiol. comp. et oecol.* **4**, 329–345. Food distribution and larval size in cultures of the ant *Myrmica rubra* (L.).

Brian, M. V. (1958). *Proc. 10th int. Congr. Ent.* **2**, 497–502. The evolution of queen control in the social Hymenoptera.

Brian, M. V. (1962). *Insectes sociaux* **9**, 295–310. Studies of caste differentiation in *Myrmica rubra* (L.). 5 — Social conditions affecting early larval differentiation.

Brian, M. V. (1963). *Insectes sociaux* **10**, 91–102. Studies of caste differentiation in *Myrmica rubra* (L.). 6 — Factors influencing the course of female development in the early third instar.

Brian, M. V. (1964a). *Symp. Zool. Soc. Lond.* **14**, 13–38. Caste differentiation in social insects.

Brian, M. V. (1964b). *J. Anim. Ecol.* **33**, 451–461. Ant distribution in a southern English heath.

Brian, M. V., and Brian, A. D. (1948). *Ent. mon. Mag.* **84**, 193–198. Nest construction by queens of *Vespula sylvestris* (Scop.) (Hym., Vespidae).

Brian, M. V., and Brian, A. D. (1949). *Trans. R. ent. Soc. Lond.* **100**, 393–409. Observations on the taxonomy of the ants *Myrmica rubra* (L.) and *Myrmica laevinodis* (Nylander) (Hym., Formicidae).

Brian, M. V., and Brian, A. D. (1951). *Trans. R. ent. Soc. Lond.* **102**, 303–330. Insolation and ant population in the west of Scotland.

Brian, M. V., and Brian, A. D. (1952). *Trans. R. ent. Soc. Lond.* **103**, 1–26. The wasp *Vespula sylvestris* (Scop.): Feeding, foraging, and colony development.

Brian, M. V., and Brian, A. D. (1955). *Evolution* **9**, 280–290. On the two forms macrogyna and microgyna of the ant *Myrmica rubra* (L.).

Brian, M. V., and Carr, C. A. H. (1960). *J. Ins. Physiol.* **5**, 81–94. The influence of the queen on brood rearing in ants of the genus *Myrmica*.

Brian, M. V., and Hibble, J. (1963a). *Insectes sociaux* **10**, 71–82. Larval size and the influence of the queen on growth in *Myrmica*.

Brian, M. V., and Hibble, J. (1963b). *J. Ins. Physiol.* **9**, 25–34. 9 – oxodec-*trans*-2. enoic acid and *Myrmica* queen extracts tested for influence on brood in *Myrmica*-

Brian, M. V., and Hibble, J. (1964). *Insectes sociaux* **11**, 223–238. Studies of caste differentiation. 7 — Caste bias, queen age and influence.

Brown, E. S. (1959). *Bull. Ent. Res.* **50**, 523–558. Immature nutfall of coconuts in the Solomon Islands. II. Changes in ant populations and their relation to vegetation.

Brown, W. L., Jr., and Wilson, E. O. (1956). *Syst. Zool.* **5**, 49–64. Character displacement.

Browning, T. O. (1963). "Animal Populations." Hutchinson, London.

Bruns, H. (1957). *Zeitschr. F. ang. Ent.* **40**, 175–181. Untersuchungen über den Einfluss von Waldameisen–Kolonien (*Formica rufa*) auf die Siedlungsdichte höhlenbrütender Vögel.

Bruns, H. (1959). *Biol. Abhandl.* **22–23**, 3–52. Siedlungsbiologische Untersuchungen in einförmigen Kiefernwäldern.

Bruns, H. (1960a). *Aus dem Walde* **4**, 26–72. Die künstliche Ansiedlung und Entwicklung von Kolonien der Roten Waldameise (*Formica polyctena* bzw. *rufa*) in dem Cloppenburger Schadgebiet der Kl. Fichtenblattwespe (*Pristiphora abietina*) 1952–59.

Bruns, H. (1960b). *Entomophaga* **5**, 77–80. Ueber die Beziehungen zwischen Waldvögeln und Waldameisen.

Bruns, H. (1961). *Naturw. Rundschan* **14**, 95–103. Die wirtschaftliche Bedeutung der Vögel im Walde. Stand der Forschung u. die Beziehungen zwischen Vögeln und Insekten.

Buchli, H. (1950). *Physiol. comp.* **2**, 145–160. Recherche sur la fondation et le développement des nouvelles colonies chez le termite lucifuge (*Reticulitermes lucifugus* Rossi).

Buchner, R. (1959). *Z. Bienenforsch.* **4**, 179–185. Ueber das Verhalten von Bienen und Waldameisen an einem gemeinsamen Futterplatz.

Butler, C. G. (1940). *Bee World* **21**, 9–10. The ages of the bees in a swarm.

Butler, C. G. (1954). "The World of the Honey-bee." Collins, London.

Butler, C. G. (1956). *Ann. Rev. Ent.* **1**, 281–298. Some recent advances in apicultural research.

Butler, C. G. (1957). *Insectes sociaux* **4**, 211–223. The process of queen supersedure in colonies of honey-bees (*Apis mellifera* Linn.).

Butler, C. G. (1958). *Cent. Ass. of Bee-Keepers* **1–12**. Queen supersedure and swarming.

Butler, C. G. (1963). *Symp. R. ent. Soc. Lond.* (**2**), 6–73. Pheromones in sexual processes in insects.

Cale, G. H. (1952). "Oviposition Rates and Viability of Eggs in *Apis mellifera* L." Thesis, Iowa State College (unpub.).

Chapman, J. A. (1963). *Ecology* **44**, 766–767. Predation by *Vespula* wasps on hilltop swarms of winged ants.

Chauvin, R. (1962). *Insectes sociaux* **9**, 311–321. Observations sur les pistes de *Formica polyctena*.

Chauvin, R. (1964). *Insectes sociaux* **11**, 1–20. Expériences sur "l'apprentissage par equipe" du labyrinthe chez *Formica polyctena*.

Chen, S. C. (1937a). *Physiol. Zool.* **10**, 420–436. Social modifications of the activities of ants in nest building.

Chen, S. C. (1937b). *Physiol. Zool.* **10**, 437–455. The leaders and followers among the ants in nest building.

Clark, P. J., Eckstrom, P. T., and Linden, C. L. (1964). *Ecology* **45**, 367–372. On the number of individuals per occupation in a human society.

Cole, L. C. (1954). *Quart. Rev. Biol.* **29**, 103–137. The population consequences of life-history phenomena.

Collingwood, C. A. (1958a). *Proc. R. Irish Acad.* B**59**, 213–219. A survey of Irish Formicidae.

Collingwood, C. A. (1958b). *Proc. R. ent. Soc.* A**33**, 65–75. Ants of the genus *Myrmica* in Britain.

Collingwood, C. A. (1959). *Scottish Naturalist* **70**, 12–21. Ants in the Scottish Highlands.

Combes, M. (1937). *C.R. Acad. Sci. Paris.* **204**, 1674–1675. Existence probable d'une élite non differenciée d'aspect constituant les veritables ouvrières chez les *Formica*.

Creighton, W. S., and Crandall, R. H. (1954). *Biol. Review, City College of New York.* **16**, 2–6. New data on the habits of *Myrmecocystus melliger* Forel.

Cumber, R. A. (1949a). *Trans. R. ent. Soc. Lond.* **100**, 1–45. The biology of humble-bees, with special reference to the production of the worker caste.

Cumber, R. A. (1949b). *Proc. R. ent. Soc.* **24**, 119–127. Humble-bee parasites and commensals found within a thirty-mile radius of London.

Cumber, R. A. (1953). *N.Z. J. Sci. Tech.* B**34**, 227–240. Some aspects of the biology and ecology of humble-bees bearing upon the yields of red-clover seeds in New Zealand.

Darchen, R. (1964). *Insectes sociaux* **11**, 141–157. Biologie de *Vespa orientalis*. Les premiers stades de développement.

Deleurance, E.-P. (1950). *Colloque International, Paris.* Le polymorphisme social et son déterminisme ches les guêpes.

Deleurance, E.-P. (1957). *Ann. Sc. nat., Zool.* **19**, 91–222. Contribution à l'étude biologique des *Polistes* (Hymenoptères, Vespidés). I. L'activité de construction.

Diver, C. (1940). *In* J. S. Huxley, "The New Systematics". 303–328. Oxford. The problem of closely related species living in the same area.

Dobrzanska, J. (1958). *Acta Biol. Exp.* **18**, 55–67. Partition of foraging grounds and modes of conveying information among ants.

Dobrzanska, J. (1959). *Acta Biol. Exp.* **19**, 55–81. Studies on the division of labour in ants, genus *Formica*.

Dobrzanska, J., and Dobrzanski, J. (1960). *Insectes sociaux* **7**, 1–8. Quelques nouvelles remarques sur l'éthologie de *P. rufescens*.

Dobrzanska, J., and Dobrzanski, J. (1962). *Acta Biol. Exp.* **22**, 269–277. Quelques observations sur les luttes entre différentes espèces de fourmis.

Dobrzanski, J. (1961). *Acta Biol. Exper.* **21**, 53–73. Sur l'éthologie guerrière de *Formica sanguinea* Latr. (Hyménoptèra, Formicidae).

Dobrzanski, J. (1965). *Acta Biol. Exper.* **25**, 59–71. Genesis of social parasitism among ants.

+ Dreyer, W. A. (1942). *Ecology* **23**, 486–490. Further observations on the occurrence and size of ant mounds with reference to their age.

Dreyer, W. A., and Park, T. (1932). *Psyche* **39**, 127–133. Local distribution of *Formica ulkei* mound nests with reference to certain ecological factors.

Duncan, C. D. (1939). *Stanford Univ. Publ. Biol. Sci.* **8**, 109 pp. A contribution to the biology of the North American Vespine wasps.

Duncan-Weatherley, A. H. (1953). *Australian J. Zool.* **1**, 178–192. Some aspects of the biology of the mound ant, *Iridomyrmex detectus* (Smith).

Eckstein, K. (1937). *Mitt. Forstwirt. u. Forstwiss* **8**, 635–685. Die Nester der Walda-meisen *Formica rufa* (L.), *F. truncicola* (Nyl.) und *F. exsecta* (Nyl.).

Elton, C. (1927). "Animal Ecology." New York, Macmillan. London, Sidgwick & Jackson.

Elton, C. S. (1932). *J. Anim. Ecol.* **1**, 69–76. Territory among wood ants (*Formica rufa* L.) at Picket Hill.

Elton, C. S. (1958). "The Ecology of Invasions by Animals and Plants." Methuen, London.

+ Elton, C. S., and Miller, R. S. (1954). *J. Ecol.* **42**, 460–496. An ecological survey of animal communities: with a practical system of classifying habitats by structural characters.

Elton, E. T. G. (1958). *Proc. 10th. int. Congr. Ent.* **4**, 573–578. The artificial establishment of wood-ant colonies for biological control in the Netherlands.

+ Emerson, A. E. (1939). *Ecol. Mongr.* **9**, 287–300. Populations of social insects.

Esch, H. (1956). *Experientia* **12**, 439–441. The elements of distance communication in the dances of honey-bees.

Eskilsson, L., and Fridén, F. (1962). "Försök och Undervisning," 45–54. Pollinering och frösättning.

Farrar, C. L. (1934). *Glean. Bee Cult.* **62**, 276–278. Bees must have pollen.

Farrar, C. L. (1936). *Amer. Bee J.* **76**, 452–454. Influence of pollen reserves on the surviving population of overwintered colonies.

Forel, A. (1928). "The Social World of the Ants." Putnam, London and New York.

Fox-Wilson, G. (1946). *Proc. R. ent. Soc. Lond.* (A) **21**, 17–27. Factors affecting populations of social wasps, *Vespula* species, in England (Hymenoptera).

Free, J. B. (1955). *Brit. J. anim. Behav.* **3**, 147–153. The behaviour of egg-laying workers of bumble-bee colonies.

Free, J. B. (1957). *Proc. R. ent. Soc.* **32**, 182–184. The effect of social facilitation on the ovary development of bumble-bee workers.

Free, J. B. (1960). *Bee World* **41**, 141–151, 169–186. The pollination of fruit trees.

Free, J. B. (1963). *J. Anim. Ecol.* **32**, 119–131. The flower constancy of honey-bees.

Free, J. B., and Butler, C. G. (1959). "Bumble-bees." Collins, London.

Free, J. B., and Spencer-Booth, Y. (1959). *Proc. R. ent. Soc. Lond.* (A) **34**, 141–150. The longevity of worker honey-bees (*Apis mellifera*).

Fridén, F. (1960). *Svensk. Frötidn.* **12**, 144–150. Humlestudier inom Mälar-Hjälmarområdet år 1960.

Fridén, F. (1961). *Svensk. Frötidn.* **11**, 151–158. Humlestudier inom Mälar-Hjälmarområdet år 1961.

Gary, N. E. (1963). *J. apic. Res.* **2**, 3–13. Observations of mating behaviour in the honey-bee.

Gause, G. F. (1934). "The Struggle for Existence." Baltimore, Williams and Wilkins.

Gay, F. J., and Greaves, T. (1940). *J. Coun. sci. industr. Res. Aust.* **13**, 145–160. The population of a mound colony of *Coptotermes lacteus* (Frogg.).

Gervet, J. (1962). *Insectes sociaux* **9**, 231–263. Etudes de l'effet de groupe sur la ponte dans la société polygyne de *Polistes gallicus* L. (Hymenoptérès, Vespidés).

Gervet, J. (1964a). *Insectes sociaux* **11**, 21–40. Essai d'analyse élémentaire du comportement de ponte chez la guêpe Poliste *P. gallicus* L. (Hymen. Vesp.).

Gervet, J. (1964b). *Insectes sociaux* **11**, 343–382. Le comportement d'oophagie différentielle chez *Polistes gallicus* L. (Hymen. Vesp.).

Goetsch, W. (1939). *Zoologica, Stuttgart* **96**, 1–105. Die staaten argentinischer Blattschneiden Ameisen.

Goetsch, W. (1951). *Zool. Jb.* (*Syst.*) **80**, 64–98. Ameisen und Termiten Studien in Ischia, Capri und Neapel.

Golley, F. B., and Gentry, J. B. (1964). *Ecology* **45**, 217–225. Bioenergetics of the southern harvester ants, *Pogonomyrmex badius*.

Gontarski, H. (1953). *Z. Bienenforch* **2**, 7–10. Zur Brutbiologie der Honigbiene.

Gösswald, K. (1942). *Z. angew. Ent.* **28**, 62–124. Rassenstudien an der roten Waldameise *Formica rufa* (L.) auf systematischer, ökologischer und biologischer Grundlage.

Gösswald, K. (1951). *Zool. Jb.* **80**, 27–63. Über den Lebensablauf von Kolonien der Roten Waldameise.

Gösswald, K. (1955). *Rev. suisse Zool.* **62**, 372–386. Zur Kastenbestimmung bei Ameisen.

Gösswald, K. (1957). *Waldhygiene* **2**, 33–53. Über die biologischen Grundlagen der Zucht und Anweisung junger Königinnen der Kleinen Roten Waldameise nebst praktischen Erfahrungen.

Gösswald, K. (1958). *Waldhygiene* **2**, 234–251. Über die Auswirkung von Spechten auf die Rote Waldameise.

Gösswald, K., and Bier, K. (1953a). *Naturwissenschaften* **40**, 38–39. Untersuchungen zur Kastendetermination in der Gattung *Formica*.

Gösswald, K., and Bier, K. (1953b). *Zool. Anz.* **151**, 126–134. Untersuchungen zur Kastendetermination in der Gattung *Formica*. 2. Die Aufzucht von Geschlechtstieren bei *Formica rufa pratensis* (Retz.).

Gösswald, K., and Bier, K. (1954a). *Insectes sociaux* **1**, 229–246. Untersuchungen zur Kastendetermination in der Gattung *Formica*. 3. Die Kastendetermination von *Formica rufa rufo-pratensis minor* (Gössw.).

Gösswald, K., and Bier, K. (1954b). *Insectes sociaux* **1**, 305–318. Untersuchungen zur Kastendetermination in der Gattung *Formica*. 4. Physiologische Weisellosigkeit als Voraussetzung der Aufzucht von Geschlechtstieren im polygynen Volk.

Gösswald, K., and Bier, K. (1957). *Insectes sociaux* **4**, 335–348. Untersuchungen zur Kastendetermination in der Gattung *Formica*. 5. Der Einfluss der Temperatur auf die Eiablage und Geschlechtsbestimmung.

Gösswald, K., and Kloft, W. (1961). *Waldhygiene* **4**, 22–23. Beziehungen einiger im Walde lebender Mäuse zu Waldameisen-nestern.

Grassé, P. P. (1949). *In* "Traité de Zoologie" (P. P. Grassé, ed.) Tome IX, Masson, Paris.

Grassé, P. P., and Noirot, C. (1951). *Behaviour* **3**, 146–166. La sociotomie: Migration et fragmentation de la termitière chez les *Anoplotermes* et les *Trinervitermes*.

Grassé, P. P., and Noirot, C. (1958). *C.r. Séanc. Acad. Sci., Paris.* **246**, 1789–1795. La société de *Calotermes flavicollis* (Insecte, Isoptère), de sa fondation au premier essaimage.

Grassé, P. P., and Noirot, C. (1960). *Insectes sociaux* **7**, 323–331. L'isolément chez le termite à cou jaune (*Calotermes flavicollis* Fab.) et ses conséquences.

Grassé, P. P., and Noirot, C. (1961). *Insectes sociaux* **8**, 311–357. Nouvelles recherches sur la systématique et l'éthologie des termites champignonnistes du genre *Bellicositermes* (Emerson).

Greaves, T. (1960). *11th Int. Congr. Ent. Vienna.* 238–240. Termites in Australian forests.

Greaves, T. (1962). *Aust. J. Zool.* **10**, 630–651. Studies of foraging galleries and the invasion of living trees by *Coptotermes acinaciformis* and *C. brunneus* (Isoptera).

Haas, A. (1949). *Z. vergl. Physiol.* **31**, 281–307. Arttypische Flugbahnen von Hummelmännchen.

Hachinohe, Y., and Jimbu, M. (1958). *Bull. nat. Inst. agric. Sci. Ser. G.* (*Anim. Husb.*) **14**, 123–130. Occurrence of non-viable eggs in the honey-bee.

Hamilton, W. D. (1963). *Amer. Nat.* **97**, 354–356. The evolution of altruistic behaviour.

Hamilton, W. D. (1964a). *J. Theoret. Biol.* **7**, 1–16. The genetical evolution of social behaviour. I.

Hamilton, W. D. (1964b). *J. Theoret. Biol.* **7**, 17–52. The genetical evolution of social behaviour. II.

Harris, W. V. (1956). *Insectes sociaux* 3, 261–268. Termite mound building.

Haskins, C. P. (1945). "Of Ants and Men." George Allen & Unwin, London.

Haskins, C. P., and Haskins, E. F. (1950). *Ann. ent. Soc. Amer.* 43, 461–491. Notes on the biology and social behaviour of the archaic ponerine ants of the genera *Myrmecia* and *Promyrmecia*.

Haskins, C. P., and Haskins, E. F. (1951). *Am. Midl. Nat.* 45, 432–445. Note on the method of colony foundation of the ponerine ant *Amblyopone australis* (Erichson).

Hassanein, M. H., and Banby, M. A. el. (1960a). *Bull. Soc. ent. Egypte* 44, 291–308. Studies on the longevity of Carniolan, Caucasian and Italian honey-bee workers, with special reference to their foraging behaviour.

Hassanein, M. H., and Banby, M. A. el. (1960b). *Bull. Soc. ent. Egypte* 44, 13–22. Studies on the brood-rearing activity of certain races of honey-bee, *Apis mellifica* L.

Hayashida, K. (1959). *J. Fac. Sci. Univ. Hokkaido Ser. 6 Zool.* 14, 252–260. Ecological distribution of ants in Mt. Atusanupuri, an active volcano in Akan National Park, Hokkaido.

Headley, A. E. (1943). *Ann. ent. Soc. Amer.* 36, 743–753. Population studies of two species of ants, *Leptothorax longispinosus* (Roger) and *Leptothorax curvispinosus* (Mayr).

Headley, A. E. (1949). *Ann. ent. Soc. Amer.* 42, 265–272. A population study of the ant *Aphaenogaster fulva* ssp. *aquia* (Buckley).

Headley, A. E. (1952). *Ann. ent. Soc. Amer.* 45, 435–442. Colonies of ants in a locust wood.

Holdaway, F. G., Gay, F. J., and Greaves, T. (1935). *J. Counc. Sc. Ind. Res.* 8, 42–46. The termite population of a mound colony of *Eutermes exitiosus* (Hill).

Hölldobler, B. (1962). *Sonderdruck aus Z. ang. Entomologie* 49, 337–352. Zur Frage der Oligogynie bei *Camponotus ligniperda* (Latr.) und *Camponotus herculeanus* (L.) (Hym. Formicidae).

Holt, S. J. (1955). *J. Anim. Ecol.* 24, 1–34. On the foraging activity of the wood ant.

Huffaker, C. B. (1957). *Hilgardia* 27, 101–157. Fundamentals of biological control of weeds.

Istomina-Tsvetkova, K. P. (1957). *Zool. Zh.* 36, 1359–1370. Study of the activity of worker bees. (*Apis mellifera* L.).

Istomina-Tsvetkova, K. P. (1963). *Ent. Obozr.* 42, 127–137. Some distinguishing features of the behaviour of the worker honey-bee.

Jackson, W. B. (1957). *Ecology* 38, 276–285. Microclimate patterns in the army ant bivouac.

Jean-Prost, P. (1956). *Rev. franc. Apic.* 3, 1558–1561. Some vital statistics of bees in Provence.

Jeffree, E. P. (1955). *J. econ. Ent.* 48, 723–726. Observations on the decline and growth of honey-bee colonies.

Jeffree, E. P. (1956). *Insectes sociaux* 3, 417–422. Winter brood and pollen in honey-bee colonies.

Jeffree, E. P., and Allen, M. D. (1956). *J. econ. Ent.* 49, 831–834. The influence of colony size and of *Nosema* disease on the rate of population loss in honey-bee colonies in winter.

Kalmus, H. (1941). *Nature* 148, 228. Defence of source of food by bees.

Kalmus, H. (1964). *Symp. Zool. Soc. Lond.* 14, 1–12. Origins and general features.

Kalshoven, L. G. E. (1930). *Mededaelingen van het Instituut voor Plantenziekten* 76, Wageningen. De biologie van de Djatitermiet (*Kalotermes tectonae* Damm.) in Verband met Zijn Bestrijding.

Kalshoven, L. G. E. (1958). *Insectes sociaux* 5, 9–30. Observations on the black termites, *Hospitalitermes* spp., of Java and Sumatra.

Kalshoven, L. G. E. (1959). *Insectes sociaux* **6**, 231–242. Observations on the nests of initial colonies of *Neotermes tectonae* (Damm.) in teak trees.

Kannowski, P. B. (1959a). *Ecology* **40**, 162–165. The use of radioactive phosphorus in the study of colony distribution of the ant *Lasius minutus*.

Kannowski, P. B. (1959b). *Insectes sociaux* **6**, 115–162. The flight activities and colony-founding behaviour of bog ants in south-eastern Michigan.

Kapil, R. P. (1957). *Bee World* **38**, 258–263. The length of life and the brood-rearing cycle of the Indian bee.

Kaschef, A. H. (1959). *Insectes sociaux* **6**, 243–257. The single strain of the Egyptian honey-bee *Apis mellifica fasciata* (Latr.).

Kemper, H. (1961). *Z. angew. Ent.* **48**, 31–85. Nestunterschiede bei den sozialen Faltenwespen Deutschlands.

Kemper, H., and Döhring, E. (1961). *Z. angew. Ent.* **48**, 163–197. Zur Frage nach der Volksstärke und der Vermehrungspotenz bei den sozialen Faltenwespen Deutschlands.

Kemper, H., and Döhring, E. (1962). *Z. angew. Ent.* **49**, 227–280. Untersuchungen über die Ernährung sozialer Faltenwespen Deutschlands, insbesondere von *P. germanica* und *P. vulgaris*.

Kerr, W. E. (1951). *Anais Exola Super. Agr. "Luis de Queiroz"*. **8**, 219–354. Bases para o estudo da genética de populasções dos Hymenoptera em geral e dos Apinae sociais em particular.

Kerr, W. E., and Hebling, N. J. (1963). *Evolution* **18**, 267–270. Influence of the weight of worker bees on division of labour.

Kerr, W. E., and Laidlaw, H. H., Jr. (1956). *Adv. Genet.* **8**, 109–153. General genetics of bees.

Kerr, W. E., Zucchi, R., Nakadaira, J. T., and Butolo, J. E. (1962). *J.N.Y. ent. Soc.* **70**, 265–276. Reproduction in the social bees (Hymenoptera: Apidae).

Klomp, H. (1964). *Ann. Rev. Ent.* **9**, 17–40. Intraspecific competition and the regulation of insect numbers.

Kneitz, G. (1964). *Insectes sociaux* **11**, 105–129. Saisonales Trageverhalten bei *Formica polyctena* (Foerst.) (Formicidae, gen. *Formica*).

Lange, R. (1956). *Z. Naturforschg.* **11b**, 538–543. Experimentelle Untersuchungen über die Variabilität bei Waldameisen (*Formica rufa* L.).

Lange, R. (1957). *Verh. 4 Intern. Pflanzenschutzkongr. Hamburg* **1**, 909–911. Ueber Misserfolge bei der künstlichen Vermehrung der Roten Waldameise.

Lange, R. (1958a). *Zool. Jb.* **86**, 217–226. Über die Variabilität der Beborstung der Waldameisen (Zugleich ein Beitrag zur Systematik der *Formica rufa* Gruppe).

Lange, R. (1958b). *Z. Anz.* **161**, 238–243. Die deutschen Arten der *Formica rufa* (Gruppe).

Lange, R. (1959). *Z. ang. Ent.* **45**, 188–197. Zur Trennung von *Formica rufa* (L) und *Formica polyctena* (Först) (Hym., Formicidae).

Lange, R. (1960). *Entomophaga* **5**, 81–86. Die Systematischen Grundlagen der Waldameisenvermehrung in Deutschland.

Lavie, P. (1960). *Ann. Abeille* **3**, 103–183, 201–305. Les substances antibactériennes dans la colonie d'abeilles (*Apis mellifica* L.).

Ledoux, A. (1950). *Ann. Sci. nat. Zool.* (11) **12**, 313–461. Recherche sur la biologie de la fourmi fileuse *Oecophylla longinoda* (Latr.).

Levin, M. D. (1961). *Insectes sociaux* **8**, 195–201. Interactions among foraging honey-bees from different apiaries in the same field.

Levin, M. D., and Glowska-Konopacka, S. (1963). *J. apic. Res.* **2**, 33–42. Responses of foraging honey-bees in alfalfa to increasing competition from other colonies.

Li, C. C. (1955). "Population Genetics." Univ. Chicago Press, U.S.A.

Light, S. F., and Weesner, F. M. (1955). *Insectes sociaux* **2**, 135–146. The incipient colony of *Tenuirostritermes tenuirostris* (Desneux).

Lin, N. (1964). *Insectes sociaux* **11**, 187–192. Increased parasitic pressure as a major factor in the evolution of social behaviour in halictine bees.

Lindauer, M. (1952). *Z. vergl. Physiol.* **34**, 299–345. Ein Beitrag zur Frage der Arbeitsteilung im Bienenstaat.

Lindauer, M. (1955). *Z. vergl. Physiol.* **37**, 263–324. Schwarmbienen auf Wohnung-suche.

Lindauer, M. (1961). "Communication among Social Bees." Harvard University Press, Cambridge, Mass.

Lindauer, M., and Kerr, W. E. (1960). *Bee World* **41**, 29–41, 65–71. Communication between the workers of stingless bees.

Lövgren, B. (1958). *Bull. Math. Biophys.* **20**, 119–148. A mathematical treatment of the development of colonies of different kinds of social wasps.

Lüscher, M. (1951). *Acta trop.* **8**, 36–43. Beobachtungen über die Koloniegründung bei verschiedenen afrikanischen Termitenarten.

Lüscher, M. (1956). *Insectes sociaux* **3**, 273–276. Die Lufterneuerung im Nest der Termite *Macrotermes natalensis* (Haviland).

Lüscher, M. (1961). *Symp. R. ent. Soc. Lond.* **1**, 57–67. Social control of polymorphism in termites.

Marikovsky, P. I. (1956). *Proc. Inst. Zool. Ac. Sci. Kirghiz. S.S.R.* **5**, 89–108. Observations on the biology of the ants *Camponotus herculeanus* and *Formica rufa* in mountainous forests of Kirghizia.

Marikovsky, P. I. (1961). *Insectes sociaux* **8**, 23–30. Material on sexual biology of the ant *Formica rufa* L.

Marikovsky, P. I. (1962a). *Insectes sociaux* **9**, 173–179. On some features of behaviour of the ants *Formica rufa* L. infected with fungous disease.

Marikovsky, P. I. (1962b). *Ent. Rev.* **1**, 47–51. On intraspecific relations of *Formica rufa* L.

Marikovsky, P. I. (1963). *Insectes sociaux* **10**, 119–128. The ants *Formica sanguinea* (Latr.) as pillagers of *Formica rufa* (Lin.) nests.

Marikovsky, P. I. (1965). *Insectes Sociaux* **12**, 63–70. Colonies of yellow ants (*Lasius flavus* De Geer) as theatre of struggle between nest colonies of other ant species.

Martin, P. (1963). *Insectes sociaux* **10**, 13–42. Die Steuerung der volksteilung beim Schwärmen der Bienen Zugleich ein Beitrag sum Problem der Wanderschwärme.

Maschwitz, U. W. (1964). *Nature* **204**, 324–327. Alarm substances and alarm behaviour in social Hymenoptera.

Masne, G. le (1961a). *C. r. Séanc. Acad. Sci., Paris* **253**, 1356–1357. Recherches sur la biologie des animaux myrmécophiles: observations sur le régime alimentaire de *Paussus favieri* (Fairm.) hôte de la fourmi *Pheidole pallidula* (Nyl.).

Masne, G. le (1961b). *C. r. Séanc. Acad. Sci., Paris* **253**, 1621–1623. Recherches sur la biologie des animaux myrmécophiles: l'adoption des *Paussus favieri* (Fairm.) par une nouvelle société de *Pheidole pallidula* (Nyl.).

Maurizio, A. (1946). *Beih. schweiz. Bienenztg.* **2**, 1–48. Beobachtungen über die Lebensdauer und den Futterverbrauch gefangen gehaltener Bienen.

Maurizio, A. (1961). *Gerontologia* **5**, 110–128. Lebensdauer und Altern bei der Honig-biene (*Apis mellifera* L.).

Mauermayer, G. (1954). *Arch. Bienenk.* **31**, 31–41. Investigations on the relation between the activity and length of life of honey-bee workers.

Meyer, W. (1956). *Insectes sociaux* **3**, 303–324. Arbeitsteilung in Bienenschwarm.

Medler, J. T. (1957). *Insectes sociaux* 4, 245–252. Bumble-bee ecology in relation to the pollination of alfalfa and red clover.

Michener, C. D. (1958). *Proc. 10th int. Congr. Ent.* 2, 441–447. The evolution of social behaviour in bees.

Michener, C. D. (1962). *Insectes sociaux* 9, 355–373. Biological observations on the primitively social bees of the genus *Allodapula* in the Australian region (Hymenoptera, Xylocopinae).

Michener, C. D. (1964). *Insectes sociaux* 11, 317–342. Reproductive efficiency in relation to colony size in Hymenopterous societies.

Michener, C. D., and Michener, M. H. (1951). "American Social Insects." New York, Van Nostrand.

Michener, C. D., and Laberge, W. E. (1954). *Psyche, Camb. Mass.* 61, 63–67. A large *Bombus* nest from Mexico.

Michener, C. D., and Wille, A. (1961). *Kansas Univ. Sci. Bull.* 42, 1123–1202. The bionomics of a primitively social bee, *Lasioglossum inconspicuum.*

Mikhailov, K. I., and Taranov, G. F. (1961). *Zoologichesky Zhornal* 40, 1485–1494. On the gas exchange in the club of hibernating bees.

Milne, A. (1961). *Symp. Soc. Exper. Biol.* 15, 40–61. Definition of competition among animals.

Miyamoto, S. (1960). *Insectes sociaux* 7, 39–56. Observations on the behaviour of *Bombus diversus* Smith. (Biological studies on Japanese bees, XIII.)

Moeller, F. E. (1958). *Amer. Bee J.* 98, 401–402. Relation between egg-laying capacity of queen bee and populations and honey production of their colonies.

Montagner, H. (1962). *Ann. Abeille* 5, 233–246. Essais préliminaires de mesure de la capacité d'élevage dans la ruche.

Morimoto, R. (1954a). *Sci. Bull. Fac. Agric. Kyushu* 14, 337–353. On the nest development of *Polistes chinensis antennalis* Pérez. I. (Studies on the social Hymenoptera of Japan. III.)

Morimoto, R. (1954b). *Sci. Bull. Fac. Agric. Kyushu* 14, 511–522. On the nest development of *Polistes chinensis antennalis* Pérez. II. (Studies on the social Hymenoptera of Japan. IV.)

Morimoto, R. (1954c). *Sci. Bull. Fac. Agric. Kyushu* 14, 523–533. On the nest development of *Polistes chinensis antennalis* Pérez. III. Relation between the removal of eggs and larvae from the nest and the oviposition of the founding female. (Studies on the social Hymenoptera of Japan. V.)

Morimoto, R. (1959). *Sci. Bull. Fac. Agric. Kyushu* 17, 99–113. On the nesting activity of the founding female of *Polistes chinensis antennalis* Pérez. I. (Studies on the social Hymenoptera of Japan. VI.)

+Morris, R. F. (1959). *Ecology* 40, 580–588. Single-factor analysis in population dynamics.

Morse, R. A., and Gary, N. E. (1961). *Bee World* 42, 179–181. Insect invaders of the honey-bee colony.

Moure, J. S., Nogueira-Neto, P., and Kerr, W. E. (1958). *Proc. 10th int. Congr. Ent.* 2, 481–493. Evolution problems among *Meliponinae* (Hymenoptera, Apidae).

Muir, D. A. (1954). *Nature* 173, 688. Ants *Myrmica rubra* (L.) and *M. scabrinodis* (Nylander) as intermediate hosts of a cestode.

Nelmes, E. (1938). *J. Anim. Ecol.* 7, 74–104. A survey of the distribution of the wood ant (*Formica rufa*) in England, Wales, and Scotland.

Nilsson, J. (1959). *Svensk. Frötidn.* 28, 25–28. Iakttagelser på klöverfältet.

Nogueira-Neto, P. (1954). *Arch. Mus. nac. Rio de J.* 42, 419–451. Bionomic notes on Meliponins. III. On swarming (Hymenoptera-Apoidea).

Nogueira-Neto, P. (1964). *Bee World* **45**, 119–121. The spread of a fierce African bee in Brazil.

Noirot, C. (1959). *Ann. Soc. R. Zool. Belg.* **89**, 151–169. Remarques sur l'écologie des termites.

Noirot, C. (1960). "Verh. XI int. Kongr. Ent. Wien" **1**, 583–585. Le cycle saisonnier chez les termites.

Noirot, C., and Bodot, P. (1964). *C.r. Séanc. Acad. Sci., Paris* **258**, 3357–3359. L'essaimage d'*Allognathotermes hypogeus* Silv. (Isoptera, Termitidae).

Noirot, C., and Noirot-Timothee, C. (1962). "4th Congr. U.I.E.I.S., Pavia" **11**, 180–188. Construction et reconstruction du nid chez *Cubitermes fungifaber* Sjöst.

Nolan, W. J. (1925). *Bull. U.S. Dep. Agric.* **1349**, 1–56. The brood-rearing cycle of the honey-bee.

Odum, E. P., and Pontin, A. J. (1961). *Ecology* **42**, 186–188. Population density of the underground ant, *Lasius flavus*, as determined by tagging with P^{32}.

Otto, D. (1958a). *Wiss. Abh. Dtsch. Akad. Landwirtschaftswiss. Berlin Nr. 30 Akademie-verlag Berlin 166 S.* Ueber die Arbeitsteilung im Staate von *Formica rufa rufo-pratensis minor* (Gössw.) und ihre verhaltensphysiologischen Grundlagen.

Otto, D. (1958b). *Waldhygiene* **2**, 114–118. Die ortstreue der Blattlausbesucher von *Formica rufa* (L.).

Otto, D. (1960). *Biol. Zbl.* **79**, 719–739. Statistische Untersuchungen über die Beziehungen zwischen Königinnenzahl und Arbeiterinnengrösse bei den Roten Waldameisen ("engere *Formica rufa* L. — Gruppe").

Paraschivescu, D. (1963). *Comunicarile Academiei Republicii Populare Romîne.* **13**, 303–314. Contributii la studiul relatiilor interspecifice la formicide (Hymenoptera, Formicidae).

Park, T. (1954). *Physiol. Zool.* **27**, 177–238. Experimental studies of interspecies competition. 2. Temperature, humidity, and competition in two species of *Tribolium*.

Pavan, M. (1959). *Ministero dell' Agricoltura e Foreste, Collana Verde* **4**, 5–78. Attivita Italiano per la lotta biologica con formiche del gruppo *Formica rufa* contro gli insetti dannosi alle foreste.

Pavan, M. (1962). *Quaderno* **58**, 3–42. Premesse e attuazioni per l'utilizzazione delle Formiche del gruppo *Formica rufa* per la difesa delle foreste.

Peacock, A. D. (1950). *Ent. mon. Mag.* **86**, 294–298. Studies in Pharaoh's ant, *Monomorium pharaonis* (L.) 4. Egg production.

Peacock, A. D., and Baxter, A. T. (1950). *Ent. mon. Mag.* **86**, 171–178. Studies in Pharaoh's ant, *Monomorium pharaonis* (L.). 3. Life history.

Peacock, A. D., Hall, D. W., Smith, I. C., and Goodfellow, A. (1950). *Dept. Agric. Scot., Misc. Publ.* 17, 51 pp. The biology and control of the ant pest *Monomorium pharaonis* (L.).

Pickles, W. (1937). *J. Anim. Ecol.* **6**, 54–61. Populations, territories, and biomasses of ants at Thornhill, Yorkshire, in 1936.

Pickles, W. (1938). *J. Anim. Ecol.* **7**, 370–380. Populations, territories, and biomasses of ants at Thornhill, Yorkshire, in 1937.

Plateau-Quénu, C. (1962). *J. apic. Res.* **1**, 41–51. Biology of *Halictus marginatus* Brullé.

Plateau-Quénu, C. (1964). *Insectes sociaux* **11**, 91–95. Sur quelques traits de la biologie de *Halictus calceatus* (Scopoli).

Pohl, L. (1957). *Insectes sociaux* **4**, 349–363. Vergleichende anatomisch-histologische Untersuchungen an *Lepisma saccharina* Linné und der Myrmecophilen *Atelura formicaria* Heyden. (Beitrag zur Myrmecophilie, Erster Abschnitt).

Poldi, B. (1963). "4th Congress U.I.E.I.S. Pavia" **12**, 132–199. Studi sulla fondazione dei nidi nei Formicidi. 1. *Tetramorium caespitum* (L.).

Pontin, A. J. (1958). *Ent. mon. Mag.* **94**, 9–11. A preliminary note on the eating of aphids by ants of the genus *Lasius* (Hym., Formicidae).

Pontin, A. J. (1960a). *Insectes sociaux* **7**, 227–230. Field experiments on colony foundation by *Lasius niger* (L.) and *L. flavus* (F.) (Hym., Formicidae).

Pontin, A. J. (1960b). *Ent. mon. Mag.* **96**, 198–199. Observations on the keeping of aphid eggs by ants of the genus *Lasius*.

Pontin, A. J. (1961a). *Ent. mon. Mag.* **97**, 135–137. The prey of *Lasius niger* (L.) and *L. flavus* (F.) (Hym., Formicidae).

Pontin, A. J. (1961b). *J. Anim. Ecol.* **30**, 47–54. Population stabilization and competition between the ants *Lasius flavus* (F.) and *L. niger* (L.).

Pontin, A. J. (1963). *J. Anim. Ecol.* **32**, 565–574. Further considerations of competition and the ecology of the ants *Lasius flavus* (F.) and *L. niger* (L.).

Poteikina, E. A. (1958). *Pchelovodstvo* **35**, 13–16. Influence of autumn brood rearing on the condition of bees in the spring.

Poteikina, E. A. (1961). *Pchelovodstvo* **38**, 15–16. How bees winter that have not fed brood in the autumn.

Raignier, A. (1948). *Cellule, Louvain* **51**, 281–368. L'économie thermique d'une colonie polycalique de la fourmi des bois (*Formica rufa polyctena* Först.).

Raignier, A. (1952). "Vie et moeurs des Fourmis." Payot, Paris.

Raignier, A. (1959). *Klasse der Wetenschappen* **21**, 3–24. Het ontstaan van kolonies en koninginnen bij de Afrikaanse trekmieren.

Raignier, A., and Boven van, J. (1955). *Annls. Mus. r. Congo belge Sér. 4to, Sci. Zool.* **2**, 1–359. Etude taxonomique, biologique et biométrique des Dorylus du sousgenre *Anomma* (Hymenoptera, Formicidae).

Rashad, S. E., and Parker, R. L. (1958). *Trans. Kans. Acad. Sci.* **61**, 237–248. Pollen as a limiting factor in brood rearing and honey production during three drought years, 1954, 1955, and 1956.

Rettenmeyer, C. W. (1962). *J. Kansas ent. Soc.* **35**, 377–384. The behaviour of millipeds found with neotropical army ants.

Rettenmeyer, C. W. (1963a). *Univ. Kansas Sci. Bull.* **44**, 281–465. Behavioural studies of army ants.

Rettenmeyer, C. W. (1963b). *Ann. ent. Soc. Amer.* **56**, 170–174. The behaviour of Thysanura found with army ants.

Ribbands, C. R. (1953). *The behaviour and social life of honey-bees*. Bee Research Association, London.

Ribbands, C. R. (1964). *Symp. Zool. Soc. Lond.* **14**, 159–168. Role of recognition of comrades in the defence of social insect communities.

Richards, O. W. (1927a). *Tromsø Mus. Arsh.* **50**, 1–32. Some notes on the humble-bees allied to *Bombus alpinus* L.

Richards, O. W. (1927b). *Trans. Ent. Soc. Lond.* **75**, 233–268. The specific characters of the British humble-bees (Hymenoptera).

Richards, O. W. (1953). "The Social Insects." Macdonald, London.

Richards, O. W., and Richards, M. J. (1951). *Trans. R. ent. Soc. Lond.* **102**, 1–170. Observations on the social wasps of South America (Hymenoptera, Vespidae).

Ronchetti, G. (1963). *Memorie della Società Entomologica Italiana* **42**, 58–86. Caratteristiche, significato ed utilizzazione forestale delle popolazioni del gruppo *Formica rufa* della Lombardia (Italia settentrionale).

Roonwal, M. L. (1954). *J. Bombay Nat. Hist. Soc.* **52**, 354–364. On the structure and population of the nest of the common Indian tree ant, *Crematogaster dohrni rogenhoferi* (Mayr.) (Hymenoptera, Formicidae).

Ruttner, F., and Ruttner, H. (1963). *Bienenvater* **84**, 297–301. Die Flugaktivität und das Paarungsverhalten der Drohnen.

Sakagami, S. F. (1959). *J. Anim. Ecol.* **28**, 51–68. Some interspecific relations between Japanese and European honey-bees.

Sakagami, S. F. (1960). *Insectes sociaux* **7**, 231–249. Ethological peculiarities of the primitive social bees, *Allodape* Lepeltier and allied genera.

Sakagami, S. F., and Hayashida, K. (1960). *Insectes sociaux* **7**, 57–98. Biology of the primitive social bee *Halictus duplex* Dala Torre. II. Nest structure and immature stages.

Sakagami, S. F., and Hayashida, K. (1961). *Jour. Fac. Sci. Hokkaido Univ. Ser. 6, Zool.* **14**, 639–682. Biology of the primitive social bee *Halictus duplex* Dala Torre. III. Activities in spring solitary phase.

Sakagami, S. F., and Hayashida, K. (1962). *Anim. Behav.* **10**, 96–104. Work efficiency in heterospecific ant groups composed of hosts and their labour parasites.

Sakagami, S. F., and Oniki, Y. (1963). *Jour. Fac. Sci. Hokkaido Univ. Ser. 6, Zool.* **15**, 300–318. Behaviour studies of the stingless bees, with special reference to the oviposition process. I. *Melipona compressipes manaosensis* Schwarz.

Sakagami, S. F., and Zucchi, R. (1963). *Studia Ent.* **6**, 497–510. Oviposition process in a stingless bee, *Trigona (Scaptotrigona) postica* Latr. (Hym.).

Salt, G. (1961). *Symp. Soc. exper. Biol.* **15**, 96–119. Competition among insect parasitoids.

Sands, W. A. (1956). *Insectes sociaux* **3**, 531–536. Factors affecting the survival of *Odontotermes badius* (Hav.).

Sands, W. A. (1960). *Insectes sociaux* **7**, 251–263. The initiation of fungus comb construction in laboratory colonies of *Ancistrotermes guineensis* (Silvestri).

Sands, W. A. (1961). *Insectes sociaux* **8**, 177–188. Nest structure and size distribution in the genus *Trinervitermes* (Isoptera, Termitidae, Nasutitermitinae) in West Africa.

Satchell, J. E., and Collingwood, C. A. (1955). *N.W. Naturalist* **3**, 23–29. The wood ants of the English Lake District.

Scherba, G. (1958). *Insectes sociaux*, **5**, 201–213. Reproduction, nest orientation and population structure of an aggregation of mound nests of *Formica ulkei* (Emery) (Formicidae).

Scherba, G. (1961). *J. N.Y. ent. Soc.* **69**, 71–78. Nest structure and reproduction in the mound-building ant *Formica opaciventris* (Emery) in Wyoming.

Scherba, G. (1963). *J. N.Y. ent. Soc.* **71**, 219–232. Population characteristics among colonies of the ant *Formica opaciventris* (Emery) (Hymenoptera, Formicidae).

Scherba, G. (1964). *Anim. Behav.* **12**, 508–512. Analysis of inter-nest movement by workers of the ant *Formica opaciventris* Emery (Hymenoptera: Formicidae).

Schmidt, R. S. (1960). *Insectes sociaux* **7**, 357–368. Functions of *Apicotermes* nests.

Schneirla, T. C. (1949). *Bull. Am. Mus. nat. Hist.* **94**, 1–81. Army-ant life and behaviour under dry-season conditions. 3. The course of reproduction and colony behaviour.

Schneirla, T. C. (1956). *Insectes sociaux* **3**, 49–69. A preliminary survey of colony division and related processes in two species of terrestrial army ants.

Schneirla, T. C. (1957). *Insectes sociaux* **4**, 259–298. A comparison of species and genera in the ant subfamily Dorylinae with respect to functional pattern.

Schneirla, T. C. (1963). *Anim. Behav.* **9**, 583–595. The behaviour and biology of certain nearctic army ants: springtime resurgence of cyclic function — southeastern Arizona.

Schneirla, T. C., Brown, R. Z., and Brown, F. C. (1954). *Ecol. Monogr.* **24**, 269–296. The bivouac or temporary nest as an adaptive factor in certain terrestrial species of army ants.

Schuà, L. (1955). *Insectes sociaux* **2**, 45–56. Stehen Erkrankungen und Totenfall der Bienen im Winter im Zusammenhang mit Witterungsfaktoren?

Scott, H. (1944). *Ent. mon. Mag.* **80**, 1–4. Notes on the season of 1943.

Simpson, J. (1957). *Proc. R. ent. Soc. Lond.* (A)**32**, 185–192. Observations on colonies of honey-bees subjected to treatments designed to produce swarming.

Simpson, J. (1958). *Insectes sociaux* **5**, 77–95. The factors which cause colonies of *Apis mellifera* to swarm.

Simpson, J. (1959). *Insectes sociaux* **6**, 85–99. Variation in the incidence of swarming among colonies of *Apis mellifera* throughout the summer.

Simpson, J. (1960). *J. Agric. Sci.* **54**, 195. The age of queen honey-bees and the tendency of their colonies to swarm.

Simpson, J., and Riedel, I. B. M. (1963). *J. apic. Res.* The factor that causes swarming by honey-bee colonies in small hives.

Simpson, J., Riedel, I. B. M., and Inge, B. M. (1964). *Behaviour* **23**, 140–148. The emergence of swarms from *Apis mellifera* colonies.

Skaife, S. H. (1954). "African Insect Life." Longmans, London, Cape Town, and New York.

Sladen, F. W. L. (1912). "The Humble-bee, its Life History and how to Domesticate it." Macmillan, London.

Smith, J. Maynard (1964). *Nature* **201**, 1145–1147. Group selection and kin selection.

Solomon, M. E. (1964). *Adv. Ecol. Res.* **2**, 1–58. Analysis of processes involved in the natural control of insects.

Soulié, J. (1962). *Ann. Sci. nat.* **4**, 669–826. Recherches écologique sur quelques espèces de fourmis du genre *Crematogaster* de l'ancien monde (Europe, Afrique du Nord, Asie du Sud-Est).

Steyn, J. J. (1958). *Proc. 10th Int. Congr. Ent.* **4**, 589–594. The effect of ants on citrus scales at Letaba, South Africa.

Stumper, R. (1962). *Insectes sociaux* **9**, 329–333. Sur un effet de groupe chez les femelles de *Camponotus vagus* (Scopoli).

Subbiah, M. S., and Mahadevan, V. (1957). *Indian J. vet. Sci.* **27**, 153–154. *Vespa cincta* (Fabr.) — a predator of the hive bees and its control.

Sudd, J. H. (1957). *Br. J. Anim. Behav.* **5**, 104–109. Communication and recruitment in Pharaoh's ant, *Monomorium pharaonis* (L.).

Sudd, J. H. (1958). *15th Int. Congr. Zool.* Sect. 11, Paper 18. The foraging methods of some myrmicine ants in Nigeria.

Sudd, J. H. (1959). *Nature* **183**, 1588. Interaction between ants on a scent trail.

Sudd, J. H. (1960). *Anim. Behav.* **8**, 67–75. The foraging method of Pharaoh's ant, *Monomorium pharaonis* (L.).

Talbot, M. (1943). *Ecology* **24**, 31–44. Population studies of the ant *Prenolepsis imparis* (Say.).

Talbot, M. (1945). *Ann. ent. Soc. Amer.* **38**, 365–372. Population studies of the ant *Myrmica schencki* ssp. *emeryana* (Forel).

Talbot, M. (1948). *Ecology* **29**, 316–325. A comparison of two ants of the genus *Formica*.

Talbot, M. (1951). *Ann. ent. Soc. Amer.* **44**, 302–307. Populations and hibernating conditions of the ant *Aphaenogaster* (*Attomyrma*) *rudis* (Emery).

Talbot, M. (1953). *Contr. Lab. vertebr. Biol. Univ. Mich.* **63**, 1–13. Ants of an old-field community on the Edwin S. George Reserve, Livingston County, Michigan.

Talbot, M. (1954). *Contr. Lab. vertebr. Biol. Univ. Mich.* **69**, 1–9. Populations of the ant *Aphaenogaster* (*Attomyrma*) *treatae* (Forel) on abandoned fields on the Edwin S. George Reserve.

Talbot, M. (1956). *Psyche* **63**, 134–139. Flight activities of the ant *Dolichoderus* (*Hypoclinea*) *mariae* (Forel).

Talbot, M. (1957a). *Ecology* **38**, 449–456. Population studies of the slave-making ant *Leptothorax duloticus* and its slave, *Leptothorax curvispinosus*.

Talbot, M. (1957b). *Insectes sociaux* **4**, 375–384. Populations of ants in a Missouri woodland.

Talbot, M. (1961). *Ecology* **42**, 202–205. Mounds of the ant *Formica ulkei* at the Edwin S. George Reserve, Livingston County, Michigan.

Talbot, M., and Kennedy, C. H. (1940). *Ann. ent. Soc. Amer.* **33**, 560–577. The slave-making ant, *Formica sanguinea subintegra* (Emery), its raids, nuptial flights and nest structure.

Taranov, G. F. (1947). *Pchelovodstvo* **24**, 44–54. The occurrence and development of the swarming instinct in bee colonies.

Taranov, G. F. (1952). *Zool. Zh.* **31**, 61–71. Rules governing the flight activities of bees.

Taranov, G. F., and Mikhailov, K. I. (1960). *Pchelovodstvo* **37**, 5–10. The concentration of carbon dioxide in the winter cluster of the honey-bee.

Tevis, L., Jr. (1958). *Ecology* **39**, 695–704. Interrelations between the harvester ant *Veromessor pergandei* (Mayr) and some desert ephemerals.

Thakar, C. V., and Tonapi, K. V. (1961). *Bee World* **42**, 61–62. Nesting behaviour of Indian honey-bees. I. Differentiation of worker, queen, and drone cells on the combs of *Apis dorsata* (Fab.).

Thakar, C. V., and Tonapi, K. V. (1962). *Indian Bee J.* **24**, 27–31. Nesting behaviour of Indian honey-bees. II. Nesting habits and comb-cell differentiation in *Apis florea* (Fab.).

Vanderplank, F. L. (1960). *J. anim. Ecol.* **29**, 15–33. The bionomics and ecology of the red tree ant, *Oecophylla* sp., and its relationship to the coconut bug *Pseudotheraptus wayi* (Brown) (Coreidae).

Varley, G. C. (1963). *Proc. R. ent. Soc.* (C) **28**, 52–57. The interpretation of change and stability in insect populations.

Voûte, A. D. (1957). *Z. angew. Ent.* **41**, 172–178. Regulierung der Bevölkerungsdichte von schädlichen Insekten auf geringer Höhe durch die Nähr pflanze (*Myelophilus piniperda* L., *Retinia buoliana* Schff., *Diprion sertifer* (Geoffr.).

Wafa, A. K. (1956). *Bull. Fac. Agric. Cairo Univ.* **103**, 35 pp. Ecological investigations on the activity of the oriental hornet *Vespa orientalis*.

Wallis, D. I. (1962a). *Anim. Behav.* **10**, 267–274. Aggressive behaviour in the ant *Formica fusca*.

Wallis, D. I. (1963). *Behaviour* **23**, 149–175. The foraging behaviour of the ant *Formica fusca*.

Waloff, N. (1957). *Insectes sociaux* **4**, 391–408. The effect of the number of queens of the ant *Lasius flavus* (Fab.) (Hym., Formicidae) on their survival and on the rate of development of the first brood.

Waloff, N., and Blackith, R. E. (1962). *J. Anim. Ecol.* **31**, 421–437. The growth and distribution of the mounds of *Lasius flavus* (Fabricius) (Hym., Formicidae) in Silwood Park, Berkshire.

Way, M. J. (1953). *Bull. ent. Res.* **44**, 669–691. The relationship between certain ant species with particular reference to biological control of the coreid, *Theraptus sp.*

Way, M. J. (1954a). *Bull. ent. Res.* **45**, 93–112. Studies of the life history and ecology of the ant *Oecophylla longinoda* (Latreille).

Way, M. J. (1954b). *Bull. ent. Res.* **45**, 113–134. Studies on the association of the ant *Oecophylla longinoda* (Latr.) (Formicidae) with the scale insect *Saissetia zanzibarensis* (Williams) (Coccidae).

Way, M. J. (1963). *Ann. Rev. Ent.* **8**, 307–344. Mutualism between ants and honeydew-producing Homoptera.

Weaver, N. (1957). *Ann. ent. Soc. Amer.* **50**, 283–294. Effects of larval age on dimorphic differentiation of the female honey-bee.

Weber, N. A. (1956). *Ecology* **37**, 150–161. Fungus-growing ants and their fungi: *Trachymyrmex septentrionalis*.

Weber, N. A. (1958). *Proc. 10th Int. Congr. Ent.* **2**, 459–473. Evolution in fungus-growing ants.

Weber, N. A. (1959). *Ent. News* **70**, 85–90. The stings of the harvesting ant, *Pogonomyrmex occidentalis* (Cresson), with a note on populations (Hymenoptera).

Weber, N. A. (1962). *Nat. Hist. New York* **61**, 45–51. Insect gardeners.

Weber, N. A. (1963a). *Proc. ent. Soc. Wash.* **65**, 109. Ten kilometres of swarms of an ant.

Weber, N. A. (1963b). *Ann. Ent. Soc. Amer.* **57**, 85–89. A five-year colony of a fungus-growing ant, *Trachymyrmex zeteki*.

Weesner, F. M. (1956). *Univ. Calif. Publ. Zool.* **61**, 253–314. The biology of colony foundation in *Reticulitermes hesperus* (Banks).

Weesner, F. M. (1960). *Ann. Rev. Ent.* **5**, 153–170. Evolution and biology of the termites.

Weir, J. S. (1957). *J. exper. Biol.* **34**, 464–468. Effect of anaesthetics on workers of the ant *Myrmica*.

Weir, J. S. (1958a). *Insectes sociaux* **5**, 97–127. Polyethism in workers of the ant *Myrmica*.

Weir, J. S. (1958b). *Insectes sociaux* **5**, 315–339. Polyethism in workers of the ant *Myrmica*. (Part II.)

Weir, J. S. (1959a). *Insectes sociaux* **6**, 187–201. Egg-masses and early larval growth in *Myrmica*.

Weir, J. S. (1959b). *Physiol. Zool.* **32**, 63–77. Interrelation of queen and worker oviposition in *Myrmica*.

Wellenstein, G. (1958a). *Verh. dtsch. Ges. angew. Ent.* **14**, 109–114. Die trophobiose der Waldameisen und ihre bienenwirtschaftliche Bedeutung.

Wellenstein, G. (1958b). *Allg. Forstz.* **13**, 213–214. Versuche zur Klärung der bienenwirtschaftlichen Bedeutung der kahlrüchigen roten Waldameise.

Wellenstein, G. (1959). *Fortwiss. Cb.* **78**, 150–166. Möglichkeiten und Grenzen des Einsatzes von Krankheitserregern, Nutzinsekten und Vögeln im praktischen Forstschutz.

Wellenstein, G. (1960). *Z. angew. Ent.* **47**, 32–41. Ergebnisse vierjähriger Untersuchungen über die Steigerung der Waldbienentracht.

Wellington, W. G. (1960). *Canad. J. Zool.* **38**, 289–314. Qualitative changes in natural populations during changes in abundance.

Wenner, A. M. (1961). *J. Theor. Biol.* **1**, 324–327. Division of labour in a honey-bee colony — a Markov process?

Wenner, A. M. (1964). *Sci. Amer.* **210**, 116–124. Sound communication in honey-bees.

Weyrauch, W. (1935). *Biol. Zentrbl.* **55**, 484–524. *Dolichovespula* und *Vespa*. Vergleichende Uebersicht über zwei wesentliche Lebenstypen bei sozialen Wespen.

Wheeler, W. M. (1910). "Ants — Their Structure, Development and Behaviour." Columbia University Press, New York.

Wheeler, W. M. (1922a). "Social Life Among the Insects." London, Constable.

Wheeler, W. M. (1922b). *Bull. Amer. Mus. Nat. Hist.* **45**, 1139 pp. Ants of the American Museum Congo Expedition: a contribution to the myrmecology of Africa.

Wheeler, W. M. (1936). *Proc. Amer. Acad. Arts Sci.* **71**, 159–243. Ecological relations of ponerine and other ants to termites.

Wheeler, W. M. (1937). "Mosaics and Anomalies Among Ants." Harvard University Press, Cambridge, Mass.

Williams, R. M. C. (1959a). *Insectes sociaux* **6**, 292–304. Colony development in *Cubitermes ugandaensis.*

Williams, R. M. C. (1959b). *Insectes sociaux* **6**, 203–218. Flight and colony foundation in two *Cubitermes* species (Isoptera, Termitidae).

Wilson, E. O. (1951). *Evolution* **5**, 68–79. Variation and adaptation in the imported fire ant.

Wilson, E. O. (1953a). *Evolution* **7**, 262–263. Origin of the variation in the imported fire ant.

Wilson, E. O. (1953b). *Ann. ent. Soc. Am.* **46**, 479–495. The ecology of some North American dacetine ants.

Wilson, E. O. (1957). *Psyche* **64**, 46–50. The organization of a nuptial flight of the ant *Pheidole sitarches* (Wheeler).

Wilson, E. O. (1958a). *Evolution* **12**, 24–31. The beginnings of nomadic and group-predatory behaviour in the ponerine ants.

Wilson, E. O. (1958b). *Insectes sociaux* **5**, 129–140. Observations on the behaviour of the cerapachyine ants.

Wilson, E. O. (1959a). *Ecology* **40**, 437–447. Some ecological characteristics of ants in New Guinea rain forests.

Wilson, E. O. (1959b). *Psyche* **66**, 29–34. Communication by tandem running in the ant genus *Cardiocondyla.*

Wilson, E. O. (1962a). *Anim. Behav.* **10**, 134–147. Chemical communication among workers of the fire ant *Solenopsis saevissima* (Fr. Smith). 1. The organization of mass-foraging.

Wilson, E. O. (1962b). *Anim. Behav.* **10**, 148–158. Chemical communication among workers of the fire ant *Solenopsis saevissima* (Fr. Smith). 2. An information analysis of the odour trail.

Wilson, E. O. (1962c). *Anim. Behav.* **10**, 159–164. Chemical communication among workers of the fire ant *Solenopsis saevissima* (Fr. Smith). 3. The experimental induction of social responses.

Wilson, E. O. (1962d). *Bull. Mus. comp. Zool. Harv.* **127**, 403–421. Behaviour of *Daceton armigerum* (Latreille), with a classification of self-grooming movements in ants.

Wilson, E. O. (1963a). *Evolution* **17**, 249–253. Social modifications related to rareness in ant species.

Wilson, E. O. (1963b). *Ann. Rev. Ent.* **8**, 345–368. The social biology of ants.

Wilson, E. O., and Bossert, W. H. (1963). *Recent Progr. in Hormone Research* **19**, 673–716. Chemical communication among animals.

Wilson, E. O., and Brown, W. L., Jr. (1958). *Evolution* **12**, 211–218. Recent changes in the introduced population of the fire ant *Solenopsis saevissima* (Fr. Smith).

Woods, E. F. (1959). *Nature, Lond.* **184**, 842–844. Electronic prediction in swarming bees.

Wynne-Edwards, V. C. (1962). "Animal Dispersion in Relation to Social Behaviour." Oliver & Boyd, Edinburgh, London.

Yarrow, I. H. H. (1955). *Trans. Soc. Brit. Ent.* **12**, 1–48. The British ants allied to *Formica rufa* (L.) (Hym., Formicidae).

+ Yasuno, M. (1963). *Ecol. Rev.* **16**, 83–91. The study of the ant population in the grass-land at Mt. Hakkôda. I. The distribution and nest abundance of ants in the grassland.

Yasuno, M. (1964). *Sci. Rep. Tôhoku Univ.* **4**, Biol. 30, 43–55. The study of the ant population in the grassland at Mt. Hakkôda. II. The distribution pattern of ant nests at the Kayano grassland.

Yoshikawa, K. (1954). *J. Inst. Polytech. Osaka* **5**, 9–17. Ecological studies of *Polistes* wasps. 1. On the nest evacuation.

Yoshioka, H. (1952). *Sci. Rep. Gumma Univ.* **2**, Part 3 (Biol), 1–10. The change of body weight of the new queen and her brood of an incipient colony of the ant *Lasius niger* (L.).

Zmarlicki, C., and Morse, R. A. (1963). *J. apic. Res.* **2**, 64–66. Drone congregation areas.

AUTHOR INDEX

A

Adeli, E., 7, 69, 82
Allen, M. D., 36, 42, 76
Andrewartha, H. G., 40
Ayre, G. L., 6, 8, 58

B

Banby, M. A. el., 33, 35
Batra, S. W. T., 10, 11, 45, 76, 79
Baxter, A. T., 37
Ben-Nerya, A., 33
Bequaert, 67, 73, 103
Bernard, F., 68
Bier, K., 57
Bingefors, S., 7, 70
Birch, L. C., 40
Bitancourt, A. A., 47
Blackith, R. E., 6, 8, 48, 65, 66, 68, 78, 98
Bodenheimer, F. S., 1, 5, 23, 28, 33, 35, 36, 42, 43, 44, 61, 64
Bodot, P., 72
Bossert, W. H., 47, 75
Boven, van J., 4, 6, 8, 27, 34, 60, 76, 83, 95
Box, T. W., 9, 68
Bozina, K. D., 63
Brereton, J. Le Gay, 1, 3
Brian, A. D., 12, 23, 28, 31, 35, 37, 40, 57, 62, 63, 68, 71, 75, 76, 77, 80, 88, 90, 91, 97, 103
Brian, M. V., 6, 8, 12, 14, 16, 17, 23, 24, 25, 26, 28, 20, 30, 34, 37, 38, 39, 43, 46, 50, 51, 54, 56, 57, 58, 60, 62, 63, 68, 69, 70, 71, 78, 80, 81, 83, 88, 92
Brown, E. S., 100
Brown, F. C., 67
Brown, R. Z., 67
Brown, W. L., Jr., 88, 94
Browning, T. O., 3
Bruns, H., 7, 102
Buchli, H., 14
Buchner, R., 101

B (continued)

Butler, C. G., 5, 6, 20, 33, 46, 50, 59, 60, 67, 70, 71, 75, 80, 103
Butolo, J. E., 63

C

Cale, G. H., 33, 35
Carr, C. A. H., 37
Chapman, J. A., 105
Chauvin, R., 76, 81, 89
Chen, S. C., 48
Clark, P. J., 102
Cole, L. C., 41
Collingwood, C. A., 66, 68, 70, 88
Combes, M., 49
Crandall, R. H., 68
Creighton, W. S., 68
Cumber, R. A., 5, 13, 22, 31, 33, 37, 41, 46, 49, 55, 61, 63, 76, 79, 90, 103, 104

D

Darchen, R., 12
Davis, 6, 62
Deleurance, E. P., 11, 16, 32, 51
Diver, C., 92
Dobrzanska, J., 75, 76, 80
Dobrzanski, J., 76, 94
Döhring, E., 5, 55, 61, 62, 91
Dreyer, W. A., 64
Duncan, C. D., 63
Duncan-Weatherley, A. H., 18

E

Eckstein, K., 7
Eckstrom, P. T., 102
Elton, C. S., 6, 18, 77, 81, 82, 97, 98
Elton, E. T. G., 58
Emerson, A. E., 1
Esch, H., 75
Eskilsson, L., 7, 70

F

Farrar, C. L., 33

SUBJECT INDEX

A

Allodape spp., 23
Allodapula spp., 5, 80
Allognathotermes hypogeus, 72
Amblypone pallipes, 7
Amitermes evuncifer, 101
Ancistrotermes guineaensis, 15
Anoplolepis spp., 66, 94, 99, 100
Anoplolepis custodiens, 67, 94, 99
Anoplolepis longipes, 84, 94, 99, 100
Aphaenogaster spp., 6
Aphaenogaster rudis, 7, 58
Aphaenogaster treatae, 78
Apicotermes spp., 47
Apis spp., 20, 21, 38, 44, 45, 50, 75, 90
Apis cerana, 67, 91
Apis dorsata, 27, 67, 84, 91
Apis florea, 5, 67, 75, 84, 91
Apis mellifera, 1, 5, 7, 19, 20, 21, 22, 23,
    27, 28, 33, 35, 38, 42, 45, 47, 50, 51,
    59, 62, 63, 65, 67, 70, 71, 72, 75, 76,
    80, 81, 82, 84, 86, 87, 88, 91, 97, 101,
    104, 105, 108
Apis mellifera adansonii, 86, 87, 88
Araucomyrmex tener, 71, 86
Aristida oligantha, 68
Arrhenatherum elatior, 68
Artemisia cana, 8
Atta spp., 98
Atta sexdens, 47
Attini, 14, 96

B

Bellicositermes natalensis, 34, 101
Bombus spp., 5, 6, 11, 12, 16, 22, 23, 26,
    33, 35, 36, 38, 44, 46, 49, 55, 61, 62,
    67, 70, 71, 75, 76, 77, 79, 80, 85, 90,
    96, 103, 104, 107, 108
Bombus agrorum, 6, 31, 37, 38, 40, 42, 49,
    55, 61, 63, 103
Bombus hortorum, 91
Bombus humilis, 35

Bombus hynorum, 90
Bombus lapidarius, 6, 90
Bombus lucorum, 61, 90, 91, 97, 103
Bombus pratorum, 90
Bombus terrestris, 90
Brachypodium pinnatum, 68

C

Calluna vulgaris, 68
Calotermes flavicollis, 13, 58
Calotermitidae, 6, 13, 34, 65
Camponotus herculeanus, 94, 98
Camponotus ligniperda, 84
Camponotus vagus, 17
Cardiocondyla, 98
Carya ovata, 7
Cerapachinae, 6
Cetonia spp., 70
Coptotermes acinaformis, 78
Coptotermes brunneus, 78, 83
Cotoneaster spp., 80
Crematogaster spp., 19, 99
Crematogaster scutellaris, 14
Cryptotermes havilandi, 13
Cubitermes spp., 101
Cubitermes fungifaber, 48, 50
Cubitermes ugandensis, 13, 70, 105

D

Dacetini, 73
Dolichoderinae, 6
Dolichoderus spp., 104
Dolichoderus mariae, 62
Dolichoderus taschenbergi, 62
Dolichovespula spp., 60, 61, 62, 91
Dolichovespula sylvestris, 5, 12, 22, 63
Dorylinae, 6, 26, 73, 75, 83, 96
Dorylus spp., 95, 99, 105
Dorylus (*Anomma*), 19, 21, 27, 83
Dorylus (*Anomma*) *kohli*, 105
Dorylus (*Anomma*) *nigricans*, 34, 60, 95, 105